TOOLS
Memory
Jogger™

Generating Customer Buy-In
and Solutions that Flourish

Paula K. Martin

First Edition | GOAL/QPC

The Innovation Tools Memory Jogger™

Development Team
   Susan Griebel, *Project Leader*
   Robert N. King, *Illustrator*
   Janet MacCausland, *Illustrator | Designer*
   nSight, Inc., *Project Editor*

GOAL/QPC
12 Manor Parkway, Salem, NH 03079-2841
Toll free: **800.643.4316** or 603.893.1944
Fax: 603.870.9122
E-mail: **service@goalqpc.com**
www.MemoryJogger.org

Printed in the United States of America

First Edition
10 9 8 7 6 5 4 3 2 1

ISBN: 978-1-57681-109-2

Table of Contents

Chapters in bold are tools that consist primarily of tips for applying the content.

About the Author

Paula K. Martin is the founder of, and an executive consultant for, *Martin Training Associates*, a training and consulting company that specializes in the new matrix management, project management, new accountability, meeting management, and innovation. Paula is the coauthor of the *Project Management Memory Jogger*™ and has authored nine other books on the topics just mentioned.

Paula received her masters of science degree and then spent eight years with the R&D division of American Cyanamid Company where she was a director of New Product Development overseeing the introduction of numerous product and process innovations. Since leaving American Cyanamid in 1989, Paula has worked as a consultant in the areas of product, service, process, and organizational design/management system innovations.

Acknowledgments

The author would like to thank the following people who made major contributions to the content in this book:

Cathy Cassidy, CEO, *Martin Training Associates*—Cathy was invaluable as a sounding board for the concepts and ideas for this Jogger. Her organization provides training in various aspects of the innovation system, including innovation tools training. For more information, go to www.martintraining.com.

Valerie Hart, MFA, consultant—Valerie has been in marketing and finance for service businesses such as banking, internet services, and telecom for more than twenty years. Utilizing her extensive industry experience, she crafted many of the case study examples for the book.

If you need a writer who can easily deal with complex technical information, she's your gal!

G. Robin Henderson, Principal, *Halcro Consultancy*— Robin is an experienced statistician who has helped tremendously in making the "Factorial Design of Experiments" tool accurate and understandable. He is the author of the book, *Six Sigma Quality Improvement with Minitab*. If you need a statistician, hire him! www.halcroconsultancy.info

Tom Kling, Master Black Belt, *Dow Chemical Co.*—Tom did an amazing job of not only suggesting improvements to the content, most of which were adopted, but also correcting my many typos. Thanks Tom!

A *big thanks to the following people for helping to review the book*:

Craig Alexander, Process Optimization Engineer, *Monsanto*

Paula Alexander, Director, U.S. Marketing, *Burt's Bees®*

Lee Alphen, CFO, GOAL/QPC

Lucy Harrison, Product Development, *College Center for Library Automation*

Martha LeGare, CEO, *Gantt Group*

Dana Michaels, Project Leader, *GE Healthcare*

Howard Powell, PMP, *College Center for Library Automation*

John Slack, Principal, *Norse Enterprises, Inc.*

How to Navigate this Book

This pocket guide provides overview graphics, introductory information, visual cues, case study examples, and clear friendly language to help a team navigate its way through the process of creating successful innovations. Innovation leaders and team members will find this book a necessary reference for how to go about creating any type of innovation.

This book is not intended to be read cover to cover. Instead, it is meant to "jog your memory" about how to apply individual tools in your own innovation work.

I recommend that you read Chapters 1 through 5 before you attempt to apply the tools in order to get oriented to the concepts/terminology used in this book and the process of innovation that has been employed. Then you can pick and choose which of the twenty-two tools are most appropriate for you.

Some tools are used at multiple points in the process. These tools are divided into parts, and you'll find a guide to how these tools are applied in Chapter 2. Because they stand alone, you may encounter some redundancy between tools. Just skip any steps that seem repetitive. Every innovation project is different so you won't use every tool in every project, and there are times you might find it helpful to reuse a tool to get the information you need. Also, keep in mind that the innovation path is not linear. The path outlined in this book is a generic one and can be used as a guideline to plan your own innovation process.

To help navigate within a tool or between tools, this navigation icon

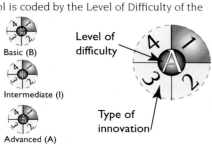

signifies that there are directions to follow about skipping steps or using another tool to gather information for that step.

Not all Tools are created equal

Seventeen tools in this Jogger begin with an overview graphic that depicts either the process that the tool uses or the output it creates. Then the purpose of the tool is described (*Why do it?*); the outputs are explained (*What does it do?*); and the steps for creating the output, including a case study example to illustrate the steps (*How do I do it?*) are outlined.

Five additional tools focus on steps to apply the concepts applicable to that tool. These tools are marked in bold in the table of contents.

To determine the Level of Difficulty and the Type of Innovation of a tool

Each tool is coded by the Level of Difficulty of the tool:

Basic (B)

Intermediate (I)

Advanced (A)

Level of difficulty

Type of innovation

In addition, each tool is coded by the Type of Innovation for which it is best suited

 a minor improvement

 major improvement

 reinvention

 invention

(See Chapter 1, for definitions of these Types of Innovation). Within the chart, the star on the right indicates an advanced tool for types 1, 2, 3, and 4 innovations. You'll find the applicable icon at the top right corner of the first page of each tool. Skip those tools that do not apply to the innovation type that your team is working on. (See page xi for a table of tools by Type of Innovation.)

To find tips look for this icon:

To find a portion of a case study example that illustrates the tool

A different case is used for each tool so that you, the reader, can see how different types of innovations can be applied using the tools. The case study example is labeled with a thumbtack at the top:

CASE STUDY

Three dots at the end of an example indicate that the example the team was working on would have continued, but is not shown here.

•••

When a table is included in the case study example, the step number for each column is indicated by a number in a circle, which indicates the step number for each column.

Innovation Type Guide to TOOLS	1	2	3	4
1. Needs Assessment	☆	☆		☆
2. Cause Analysis	☆	☆		
3. Factorial Design of Experiments	☆	☆	☆	☆
4. Paradigm Deconstruction			☆	☆
5. Context Diagram		☆	☆	☆
6. Solution Criteria & Desired Characteristics (DC) Prioritization	☆	☆	☆	
7. Basic Idea Generation	☆	☆	☆	☆
8. Generating a Breakthrough	☆	☆	☆	☆
9. Paradigm Construction			☆	☆
10. Solution Synthesis	☆	☆	☆	☆
11. Solution Filter	☆	☆	☆	☆
12. Vision Decomposition		☆	☆	☆
13. Technical Difficulty Assessment		☆	☆	☆
14. Solution Impact Risk Assessment		☆	☆	☆
15. Adoption Assessment		☆	☆	☆
16. Solution Selection	☆	☆	☆	☆
17. Solution Definition	☆	☆	☆	☆
18. Communication Plan		☆	☆	☆
19. Creative Problem Solving	☆	☆	☆	☆
20. Modeling the Solution		☆	☆	☆
21. Testing the Solution	☆	☆	☆	☆
22. Launching the Solution	☆	☆	☆	☆

ONE

WHAT IS INNOVATION?

Innovation is the process of creating a solution for a customer, which takes them from a state of dissatisfaction with the current system to a future state where they are satisfied with the solution. It moves a customer from "what is" to "what will be." We use the term *current system* generically to mean the product, process, service, or system that the customer is using before the innovation process begins.

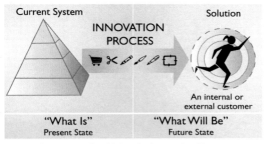

Closing the Gap Using the Innovation Process

The focus is on the customer and that customer can be outside the organization (*an external customer*)—as is the case if you're selling a product or service—or providing a public service. The customer can also be, and often is, internal to the organization.

The Innovation Process starts when the customer is dissatisfied with "what is"—with the current system or current technology. Out of this dissatisfaction comes a desire for a different future state, "what could be." The difference between what is and what could be is called the "gap." The Innovation Process closes this gap by providing a solution that meets the customer's needs as closely as possible.

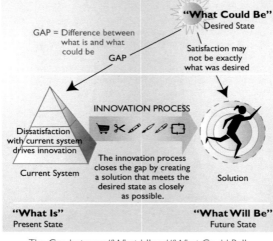

The Gap between "What Is" and "What Could Be"

Sometimes the innovation process begins with technology. An innovation is made and then a use must be found for it. That's what happened with the discovery of low-tack glue by 3M. They invented something that had no identified use, so the first step was to recognize that the anomaly—glue that didn't stay stuck—was, in fact, an invention. And then they had to find or create a need for it. It took five years, but they succeeded, and Post-it® Notes were born.

However innovation comes about, there is a gap between what is (current state) and what could be (future state). According to Robert Fritz, author of *The Path of Least Resistance*, this gap creates "structural tension," because tension always seeks resolution, it is the fuel that drives the Innovation Process forward. That gap is closed when a solution is built that meets the future need.

But building a solution is just one side of the innovation equation. The other side is getting the solution **adopted**. So, in order for something to be considered an innovation, it must a) create something new or improved—a solution, and b) be adopted by the customer (and key stakeholders). Only then has the gap been closed.

Creation and Adoption

When a team creates, it brings into existence something that didn't exist before, a new or improved product, process, service, or system. Creation isn't limited to inventing something that's never been created before, like the invention of the first personal computer. It also includes making changes to existing products, processes, services, and systems. (See Key Word Legend on page 27 for specific definitions of these terms.)

Let's look at the four different Types of Innovation from the point of view of creation:

Icon	Type	Explanation
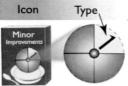		Makes a **small change** to a customer's current system, usually in the form of changing a feature or function of that system.
		Makes a **large change** to the customer's current system through a change in technology or a major change in features and primary functions.
		The customer's current system is **replaced** by an entirely new system, one that is based on a new or modified paradigm (i.e., business process reengineering). It usually is driven by customer needs that cannot be satisfied by simply improving the existing system.
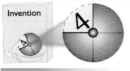		Creates a completely new **product, service, process, or system** (i.e., the invention of Post-it® Notes). It is usually driven by a technological breakthrough.

Types 1, 2, and 3 start with the customer. What do they want? What do they have now? What would ensure a brighter future for them? Type 4 creations usually start with a technological breakthrough, and then the inventor looks for a customer need that the invention can fill.

A Type 2 innovation is much more difficult to create than a Type 1. A Type 3 is even more difficult. A Type 4 is the most difficult. Reinventing and inventing are harder to do than improving because they require imagining a whole new system. And, as we move up the scale from Type 1 to Type 4, adoption also becomes increasingly difficult.

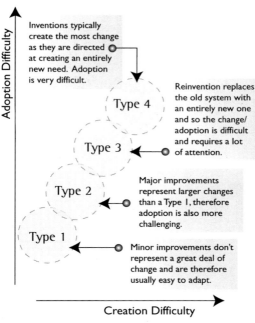

Creation and Adoption Difficulty by Innovation Type

If you haven't thought much about adoption in relationship to innovation, you're not alone. Most teams ignore adoption until the very end of the innovation process. But adoption is key to the success of any innovation! *Therefore, the team needs to be working on ensuring adoption from the minute they start down the innovation path.*

Creation requires looking at the world through the customer's eyes and answering the question, "What solution will satisfy their needs?" **Adoption** requires the same customer perspective, but the question to be answered is, "What solution are they prepared to accept?" The tools included in this Memory Jogger address both the creation and the adoption processes. Some are more focused on creation, some on adoption, and some straddle both processes.

Let's take a journey through the innovation process.

TWO

How do i navigate the innovation process?

The innovation process takes us from the identification of a need to a solution that satisfies that need. This process can be broken down into four stages: Gap Analysis; Solution Definition (which is also sometimes called conceptual design); Solution Development (which is sometimes called conceptual design); and Solution Implementation (see page 12). The process starts with the analysis of the gap. Then the best possible solution (*Solution Definition Stage*) is selected. The solution is then developed into a product, service, process, or system (*Solution Development Stage*), and then it is introduced to the customer (*Solution Implementation Stage*). In all four stages, the creation and adoption processes should happen concurrently.

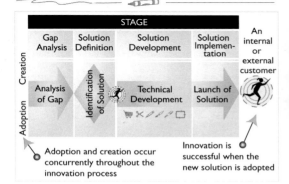

The Stages of the Innovation Process

What tools are needed in the Gap Analysis Stage?

The gap is the difference between the current "problem"—dissatisfaction with the current state—and

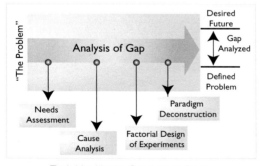

Tools Used in the Gap Analysis Stage

the desired future state (which may or may not match what is finally implemented because the solution must be feasible and adoptable). In the *Gap Analysis Stage* the team learns about What Is—what the current system is, what purpose it serves, what is causing the problems with the existing system, what paradigm the current system or technology is based on, etc.

Tool	Questions addressed by tool
Needs Assessment	• What problems are customers experiencing with the current system? • What would the customer like to see from a new system? • What are the customer's performance goals for the new system?
Cause Analysis	• What is causing of the problems the customer is experiencing with the current system?
Factorial Design of Experiments	• How does the team test its theories about the current system? • How do they conduct discovery experiments?
Paradigm Deconstruction	• What are the boundaries, concepts, rules, and assumptions of the paradigm (mental model), which underlines the current system or technology? • What problems are not being solved by the current paradigm?

What tools are needed in the Solution Definition stage?

In the first half of *Solution Definition*, the team generates options for solutions (Synthesis). In the second half they narrow down the choices (Analysis) until they've identified the best possible solution. Some of the tools are used at more than one point in the process (and so they are broken down into parts).

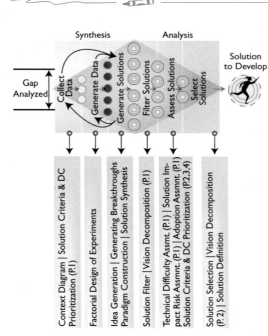

The Solution Definition Stage

Tool	Questions addressed by tool
Context Diagram	• What are the interfaces of the current system with its environment? What are the interfaces of the solution considered? • Who are the stakeholders? • When there is more than one customer group, how will their needs be prioritized? *continued on next page...*

Tool	Questions addressed by tool
Solution Criteria & (DC) Prioritization (Part 1)	• What criteria will be used to select the best possible solution?
Factorial Design of Experiments	• How can the team run experiments that test the responses of several factors at the same time?
Idea Generation	• How can the team generate lots of ideas quickly?
Generating Breakthroughs	• What are some ways of creating break-throughs in thinking?
Paradigm Construction	• After the elements of the old paradigm are deconstructed (*Paradigm Deconstruction*), how can the team build ideas for new paradigms?
Solution Synthesis	• How can the team generate ideas for solutions using all the data and information generated thus far?
Solution Filter	• How can the team narrow down the number of potential solutions to the best two to four? • What are the strengths and weaknesses of each and how can the weaknesses be overcome?
Vision Decomposition (Part 1)	• What is the long-term vision for the solution? (Part 1)
Technical Difficulty Assessment (Part 1)	• How difficult will it be to develop the solution? • How will the team overcome any technical obstacles?
Solution Impact Risk Assessment (Part 1)	• What risks might the solution pose to its environment and to the groups with which it will interface after it's launched? • What can be done to eliminate or mitigate those risks?
Adoption Assessment (Part 1)	• What could get in the way of adoption? • How can the team overcome the obstacles to adoption?

continued on next page...

Tool	Questions addressed by tool
Solution Criteria & (DC) Prioritization	• What characteristics for the final solution are desired by the customer, stakeholders, and sponsor? (Part 2) • What are the performance goals for the final solution? (Part 3) • How are competitive or benchmarked systems reformed? (Part 3 - optional) • What resources are available to develop and implement the solution? (Part 4)
Solution Selection	• Which solution best fits the selection criteria? • What charactertistics proposed by the team should be included in the selected solution, based on the resources available?
Vision Decomposition (Part 2)	• How can the vision be broken down into staged solutions?
Solution Definition	• What data collected thus far during the Innovation Process, led the team to their final recommendation for a solution? • What is the proposed contract for development?

What tools are needed in the Solution Development and Implementation Stages?

The best possible solution is selected at the end of the *Solution Definition Stage*. In the *Solution Development Stage*, the solution is actually created. Most of the effort in this phase is taken up with the *Technical Development Process* (TDP), the process through which the team creates the product, service, or process described in the *Solution Definition Document*. The *Creative Problem Solving* tool can be used at any point in the process where there is a problem. The TDP is driven by the type of technology that is needed to actually build the solution.

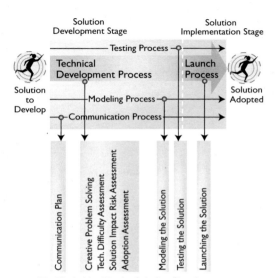

The Tools Used in the Solution Development and Implementation Stages

Tool	Questions addressed by tool
Communication Plan	• What must be communicated, when, and how, in order to move the adoption process forward?
Creative Problem Solving	• How can the team resolve the problems they encounter as they work through the development process?
Technical Difficulty Assessment	• How can the team track and update progress on resolving technical difficulties?

continued on next page...

Tool	Questions addressed by tool
Solution Impact Risk Assessment (Part 2)	• During development, how can the team track what changed to the risk profile for the solution? What new countermeasures should be implemented to reduce the risk?
Adoption Assessment (Part 2)	• How can the team track and update progress to prepare the customer and stakeholders for adoption?
Modeling the Solution	• How can the team help the customer experience the solution before it's fully built?
Testing the Solution	• Which deliverables need to be reviewed or tested before they are handed off to the next customer in the process? • How can the team test partial solutions or pilot the final solution to ensure its on the right track?
Launching the Solution	• How does the team plan for a successful solution launch?

Is the process really so linear?

The diagram of the innovation process makes the process appear to be linear, but most of the time, it's not. A team, for example, might get into the middle of solution identification and then discover they have to circle back to gap analysis in order to define a solution. Or, they may start with a vision of the solution, and skip gap analysis altogether, going right into identifying solutions that fit the vision.

Be creative with the innovation process! Use the tools that fit your team's specific needs rather than following the process from A to Z. To help guide you in deciding if a tool is a good fit for your needs, each tool has a description of what it's used for, an overview graph that depicts what the tool is all about, and bullet points on why to do it and what it does. Let these be your guide for whether the tool is a good fit in your specific process.

THREE

WHAT'S IN THE INNOVATOR'S TOOLBOX?

An innovator needs to have a number of tools in her toolbox. She needs the innovation tools described in this Memory Jogger! Some of these tools are more appropriate to beginning

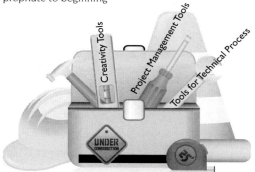

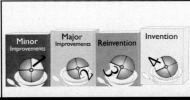

TOOL and its level of difficulty	Basic 1	Intermediate 2	Advanced 3
1. Needs Assessment	☆		
6. Solution Criteria & (DC) Prioritization	☆		
7. Basic Idea Generation	☆		
10. Solution Synthesis	☆		
11. Solution Filter	☆		
16. Solution Selection	☆		
17. Solution Definition	☆		
19. Creative Problem Solving	☆		
21. Testing the Solution	☆		
22. Launching the Solution	☆		
2. Cause Analysis		☆	
3. Factorial Design of Experiments		☆	
5. Context Diagram		☆	
8. Generating a Breakthrough		☆	
13. Technical Difficulty Assessment		☆	
14. Solution Impact Risk Assessment		☆	
15. Adoption Assessment		☆	
18. Communication Plan		☆	
20. Modeling the Solution		☆	
4. Paradigm Deconstruction			☆
9. Paradigm Construction			☆
12. Vision Decomposition			☆

innovators (basic tools) and will serve the innovator well if she is working on a minor improvement project (Type 1). As the innovator tackles more complex types of innovations, such as major improvements, reinventions, and inventions, she will need to add intermediate and then more advanced tools to her toolbox. The chart on page 16 matches the tool to its level of difficulty.

The next step in the process is to gather more advanced tools. First you need *Project Management tools*. Every innovation is a project and should be managed as such. *The Project Management Memory Jogger*™ contains a complete set of project management tools that will help any team manage any kind of innovation project.

The innovator also needs a good set of *Creativity tools*. In this Memory Jogger we discuss four creativity tools: *Idea Generation*, *Generating Breakthroughs*, *Vision Decomposition*, and *Solution Synthesis*. Because the creative process is critical to any innovation project—particularly when the team is working on a major improvement, reinvention, or invention—we recommend that you consult *The Creativity Tools Memory Jogger*™ for an expanded set of creativity tools, which will enable any team or individual to become more creative.

Finally, the innovator needs *Technical tools*—tools used in the TDP that relate specifically to the type of solution she is trying to create. For example, if she's working on an IT process, then the innovator needs to understand IT tools. If it's a construction project, she needs engineering tools. This toolset is specific to the innovation being created, and therefore is not addressed in this Jogger.

The Innovation Tools Memory Jogger™ | ©2009 GOAL/QPC

FOUR

WHAT IS A PARADIGM?

What exactly is a paradigm?

Take a brief look at the image below. What do you see?

Hold that thought a moment, and we'll get back to it.

Let's begin by defining a paradigm. Broadly speaking, it's a mental model or system of beliefs about a segment of reality. For example, Newtonian physics was the predominant mental model for physics until quantum physics replaced it at the subatomic level. A

---

paradigm can cover something very broad, like a theory of how the universe was formed or how children develop into adults; or it can be more technologically based, like a paradigm of how to manage a business process or develop a new product; or it can describe something concrete, like the paradigm of what we mean by a book. In the case of a book, our paradigm used to be that it is made out of paper, or maybe cloth (children's books), but since the end of the 1990s, the concept of a book has expanded to include electronic delivery of content.

Now back to the image on the previous page. What did you see? The letter "E"? Or did you perceive ten separate dots? Most people see the letter E because our minds automatically seek out patterns from the data in our environment. These patterns represent the paradigms that exist in our subconscious minds, which already have a paradigm for the letter "E," and we connect the dots so that the data conforms to that paradigm.

Paradigms are filters in our minds through which we perceive the world. We don't see the world as it is—the separate dots—we see the world through our own paradigms, through the filter of our beliefs. We see what we believe and then we believe what we see. It's a self-reinforcing loop, as shown here.

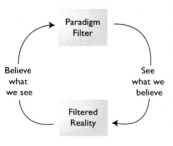

We see what we believe.

Paradigms are why we dismiss certain phenomena as being impossible, or ignore data that doesn't fit with our established mental model. The phenomena or data usually don't even get picked up by our conscious minds; if they are perceived, we dismiss them as impossible or simply not true.

Innovators cannot afford to dismiss data that don't fit, to get stuck in their own reality filters. They must see what others don't see. They must look at their own filters and then challenge their own perceptions. That's one of the keys to true innovation!

Paradigms are most important when we want to make significant improvements or if we want to reinvent or invent something new. In order to make those kinds of shifts, we must dig down to the level of the mental model or paradigm and work with the raw materials we find there—boundaries, concepts, rules, and assumptions. The more advanced *Paradigm Deconstruction* and *Paradigm Construction* tools help us do just that.

After we, as innovators, have made a shift in our paradigm, the next challenge we face is helping our customers and stakeholders shift **their** paradigm—from the one they're accustomed to and that supports their current reality, to the one that will support the new solution we're building for them. That's a key challenge of adoption. One way to help our customers and stakeholders shift their paradigms is to involve them in the creation of the solution from the very beginning. That way, their thinking evolves as the solution evolves, and adoption becomes much easier for everyone!

HOW DOES TECHNOLOGY FIT IN?

We've talked about paradigms, the mental models that form the basis of material reality. Imagine that paradigms are at the base of a pyramid. A paradigm is made up of a collection of assumptions that are then organized into concepts and rules, which, in turn, are contained by a set of boundaries. Paradigms are behind the concept of any product, service, or process, but they also form the foundation for all technology. For example, not that many years ago there was no concept of a "cell phone." If you asked

Technology Pyramid

System — Parts

Technology — Skills, Know-How

Paradigms — Boundaries, Concepts, Rules, Assumptions

someone in the 1950s if they used a cell phone, they would have looked at you as if you were from Mars, because back then, the paradigm of cell phones didn't exist.

In order for a cell phone to come into existence, two concepts had to be created: the concept of the cell phone itself—what it would look like, what features it would have, what functions it would perform—and the concept of a cellular network that would route calls through cell towers. And so, even if someone dreamed up the concepts or paradigms of cell phones/cell networks, without technology to bring them into reality, those concepts would have remained in the category of science fiction! For example, Leonardo DaVinci conceptualized many new inventions, but he didn't have the technology to actually build them. Technology is the intermediate step between a paradigm (a concept) and a system (a solution).

Technology rests on the foundation of paradigms. New technology starts with know-how, which is simply the paradigm or mental model of how to do something. Add to that know-how the skills and techniques that enable you to apply it and you have a technology. So, technology is the application of knowledge, skills, techniques, and know-how to build something. That something can be tangible, such as the building of a plane, in which case it is called a "hard" technology. Or it can be applied to the building of something intangible, such as an innovation management system, in which case it's called a "soft" technology. The tools in this book are a soft technology for creating innovations. And as is true with any technology, they'll require skill practice to apply successfully!

Technology S-Curves

The development of any technology follows a predictable path, called a technology S-curve. In the early days of a new technology, when it is at the bottom of the "S", it can solve very few problems, which was the case in the early days of the Internet (late 1960s to about 1990). Most people ignore a technology at this point. In fact, the Internet was below the radar of most companies during this early stage. But as it is applied to more and more problems, the technology continues to develop and so does its ability to solve other problems. In the 1990s, the Internet grew from almost nothing to more than 20 million nodes. This

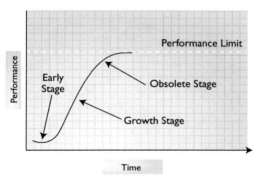

Technology Curve

was the beginning of the steep climb of its technology curve. Problems that couldn't be solved by the old technology begin to fade away as the new technology is applied. During this strong growth phase, it seems as though the technology rise will continue forever, but there are always problems that the current technology

---

(and the paradigm it's based on) can't solve either. They just aren't visible. Happily we ride the curve upward until the technology ceases to solve additional problems and we bang our collective heads against its limits. And, we keep on banging until we discover that there is another technology S-curve starting or in full swing that's making the one we've been using obsolete. We missed the boat! We're stuck with an old technology that is no longer competitive. We're in the typewriter business and everyone else has switched to word processing!

We miss the boat because we're so immersed in the paradigm of our technology that we can't see what is happening around is . . . we don't notice what our technology can't do, only what it can.

New paradigms are difficult to detect—that's why it's so important to PAY ATTENTION! Be open to what's happening on the fringes. Deconstruct the existing paradigm and start examining what the new one might look like (*Paradigm Deconstruction & Paradigm Construction* tools). Look for evidence that a new one is already in the early or even growth stages. Examine the paradigm of the technology you're currently using and consider other options when you're looking for solutions (*Solution Synthesis* tool). Be curious.

A Legend of Key Words

We'll be using some common words in a very specific way during our journey through the innovation process. Let's explore what each of these terms means relative to innovation.

Key Word	Definition
Current System	A product, service, process, or system (like IT) that the customer is using at the start of the innovation process.
Deliverable	The components that build to a solution. An **interim deliverable** is an output that is produced within a process. A **final deliverable** is produced at the end of the process.
Gap	The difference between what is now (current system) and what is desired by the customer in a future system.
Need	The customer's dissatisfaction with the current system, which then fuels the desire for a solution that will solve tomorrow's business problems.
Paradigm	A mental model or set of rules, concepts, boundaries, and assumptions about how the world operates. Paradigms underlie our current systems and technologies and are the basis for reinventing or inventing from scratch new systems and technologies.
Problem	The deviation between the current state of something and the expectation for what the state should have been.

Process	A set of steps that turns inputs into outputs. Processes are one of the targets for innovation.
Product	A tangible output of a process. Products are a target for innovation. When a new or improved product is created, a new or improved process to produce it must also be created.
Service	An act one person does for another. Services are one of the targets for innovation.
Solution	The product, service, or process being created that will solve the customer's existing problem or address a need of the customer for the future. In the early stages of the *Solution Definition* process, multiple solutions are generated and these are typically called "potential solutions." At the end of *Solution Definition*, a single solution is selected and this is the "selected solution" or "best possible solution," "best fit solution," or simply "the solution."
System	A complex combination product and/or service and/or process, such as an IT system. Systems are one of the targets of innovation.
Technology	A set of tools, techniques, skills, and know-how for creating a part of or the whole product, service, process, or system.

Key Roles in Innovation Projects

Key Word	Definition

Customer — The person(s) or group(s) who will receive and adopt the solution that is created during the innovation process. The primary adopter of the solution.

Internal Customer—The people inside the organization whose needs are driving the innovation effort and who will adopt the final solution.

External Customer—The people outside the organization who will receive the final solution and must adopt it (by purchase or use).

Customer Representatives—The person(s) selected to represent the external customer. The customer reps are usually included as members of the innovation team.

Stakeholder — Anyone who affects or will be affected by the current system or future solution, other than the customer. (Technically a customer is a stakeholder but because customers are considered in a separate category, stakeholders mean everyone other than the customer who is affected by the solution.) Stakeholders must also adopt the solution in order for it to be considered an innovation.

Key Stakeholders—These are stakeholders who have the largest stake in adopting the solution.

Innovation Leader	The person who heads up the innovation project team. Since every innovation is a project, the innovation leader is also a project manager. The innovation leader is accountable for the success of the overall innovation project.
Sponsor	The person who oversees the innovation project. The sponsor is accountable for the success of the project leader. Sometimes known as the "champion."
Team Members	Team members work with the innovation leader to come up with the developed solution. This is done during the Development Stage.

The Innovation System in Any Organization

The leadership team is accountable for creating the organizational capability to innovate, both externally (to stay competitive in the marketplace) and internally (so that the organization itself is continually renewed). The following elements are part of creating that capability:

Strategic Planning—Innovation starts with a strategic plan that is a stepped-down version of the vision the organization has for its future. In order to achieve the goals defined in the strategic plan, innovations must be created.

Innovation Steering—Innovation Steering is the process of selecting, funding, and monitoring the status of all innovation projects. Steering is done by an Innovation Steering Council (ISC) or its equivalent, which manages the portfolio of innovation projects. (Any project that produces something new—inventions, reinventions, or improvements—is an innovation project.) Projects typically are submitted to the ISC after the *Gap Analysis Stage*, then are selected (or denied) and funded for the *Solution Definition Stage*. At the end of *Solution Definition*, they are again considered for funding for the *Development Stage*. If projects make it through Development, they are usually automatically funded for Implementation. However, there are often stage gates or funding gates during Development that allow the ISC to review a project and determine if they want to continue funding it or not. Another responsibility of the ISC is to monitor the innovation portfolio to ensure that it is on track.

New Accountability System—Most accountability systems in use today are obsolete. They support individual and vertical optimization and suboptimize cross-functional team efforts. They are blame-oriented and reactive. They foster competition instead of cooperation. Innovation is a team-based endeavor that requires cross-functional cooperation; therefore it needs a new system of accountability that

☆ supports both individual and team-based endeavors

☆ is proactive

☆ focuses on lessons learned

☆ supports calculated risk taking (for more information about the new accountability visit www.martintraining.com)

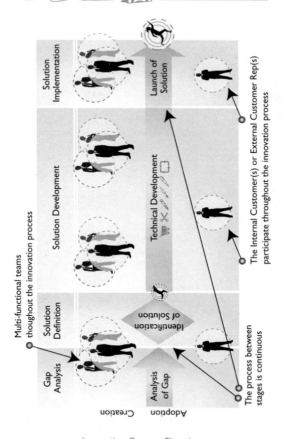

Innovation Process Showing
Team Configuration and Customer Ownership

Multi-Stage Team Structures—At any stage within the innovation process the innovation team should be a multi-stage team that includes members from both upstream as well as downstream in the process. As a project moves through the innovation process, the team configuration changes as upstream people leave and downstream people are added. This creates a seamless process, without knowledge gaps between one stage and the next.

Customer Ownership for the Innovation Effort—When the customer is external to the organization, they are represented by a customer representative. The customer or their rep should assume ownership and accountability for the innovation effort. This ensures that the customer engages in the process and it forces them to balance their desires for features and functions with the risks and the resources available to create them.

Innovation Methodology—Everyone in the organization must be trained in the organization's innovation process and the tools needed to effectively navigate it. Without an effective innovation methodology, innovation will be hit or miss.

Project Management Methodology—Since all innovations are projects (either one long project or a series of consecutive small projects), the organization needs a simple, team-based method for managing the projects, which all innovation teams can follow. Innovation leaders and team members need training so they know how to plan and manage a project.

Innovation Leadership and Sponsorship—Innovation leaders use the innovation project through one or more of its stages. The innovation leader of tomorrow will most likely come from the ranks of the project managers of today. Project management is a key skill, particularly for the *Development Stage*, but it doesn't address the creative front end of designing a solution (the *Gap Analysis* and *Solution Definition Stages*). Project managers need to be retrained to be innovation leaders. Innovation project sponsors are also important. They serve as the liaisons between the ISC and the innovation leader. They provide direction, ensure that funding is in place, remove obstacles, and provide oversight. They are accountable for the success of the innovation leader.

Senior Leadership Attitude—Senior leaders set the tone for the entire organization. They need to be

☆ open to new ideas

☆ willing to examine any paradigm and to change it when a better one comes along

☆ able to reward learning from mistakes

☆ intolerant of blame and finger-pointing (the new accountability helps with that)

☆ cooperative on setting cross-functional, cross-business priorities, and shared resources

☆ focused on the strategic plan—what's in the best interests of the entire organization

☆ willing to optimize the organization, not individual business units

The
TOOLS

1 NEEDS ASSESSMENT

Discovering the Problem

The Gap Analysis stage of an innovation project team usually begins with a *Needs Assessment*. The need that the team will be exploring in this tool is two-fold: 1) the customer's need for a solution that will remove the pain/problems they are experiencing with the current system, and 2) the customer's need for a solution that moves them forward, into the future, so they can stay competitive and survive. So, the *Needs Assessment* tool addresses both sides of the gap: the customer's current problems, and the impact of those problems on the business, and the dreams or vision for what could be and the impact that fulfilling that vision could have on the business.

A *Needs Assessment* is conducted with the actual customer (if they are internal to the organization) and/or with the customer's representatives if the customer is external. The *Needs Assessment* kicks off both the creation and adoption processes and, so, is a foundation tool of the innovation process. This is particularly true for improvement-and reinvention-type of innovations. With the needs assessment data in hand, the innovation team can chart its journey through the rest of the *Gap Analysis* and *Solution Selection* stages.

Current System Description ①

Purpose of System ②

What's Working ③
1. _____
2. _____
3. _____
4. _____

Problems with System ④
1. _____
2. _____
3. _____
4. _____

Why It's a Problem ④
_____
_____
_____

Rating ④
_____
_____
_____

Impact on Business if Nothing Changes ⑥
_____
_____

Wouldn't It be Nice... ⑤
1. _____
2. _____
3. _____
4. _____

Impact on Business ⑤
_____
_____
_____

Impact Rating ⑤
_____
_____
_____

Changes to the Busniess ⑦
_____
_____
_____

Obstacles to Adoption ⑨
1. _____
2. _____
3. _____
4. _____

Resources Available ⑨
_____
_____
_____

Type of Innovation ⑩

The Output of the Needs Assessment

Why do it?

By identifying the problems with the current system as perceived by the customer, and by identifying what the customer would like in a solution, the team begins to identify the gap between what is and what could be. This drives the creation process.

(☺) By identifying the level of pain the customer is experiencing with the current system, the team launches the adoption process.

(☺) It's the basis for creating a solution that will move the customer to a new future and is, therefore, the most fundamental of all the innovation tools.

What does it do?

(☺) Identifies the gap the customer perceives between the current system and their desires for how it could operate in the future.

(☺) Defines the impact of current system problems on the customer's business.

(☺) Explores the customer's level of "pain" with the current system and assesses their appetite for change/adoption.

(☺) Takes a first pass at defining any obstacles to adoption and lays out the resource constraints associated with the development of a solution.

(☺) Identifies the Type of Innovation that the team will be pursuing (see page xi for more information on Types of Innovation).

How do I do it?

✐ I. Describe the current system

DEFINITION: The current system is the product,

process, service, or system that the customer is currently using and that needs to change.

- Describe the current system. What are its major characteristics or features? Where does it start and end? How long has the current system been in place?

A great way to learn about the current system is to conduct a site visit or a ride-along, then hold an inquiry session (asking open-ended questions) with the customer or the customer's representative(s) to learn how the current system functions.

2. Define the purpose or function that the current system serves in terms of the customer's business

- What does the system do for the customer? What function does it perform within the context of the customer's business? Why is it important? What would happen if it ceased to function?

3. Ask the customer to define what they perceive is working with the current system

- If the customer is external to the organization, work with the internal customer representative(s) to address this step and the ones that follow.

- Which characteristics of the current system does the customer want to retain?

The Longevity Corporation, a large national hospital system, decided they wanted to reinvent the process they used to create internal and external innovations. They decided to call the effort Operation Innovation. The Executive Council chartered an innovation team to create a long-term vision of what the final innovation system at Longevity would look like and to decide which segment of it should be implemented first. The customer for Operation Innovation was the Executive Council (EC). A representative of the EC was assigned to be both the customer representative and the sponsor for the project.

The purpose of the innovation system was determined to be to: 1) ensure that Longevity continually reinvents itself, and 2) ensure that longevity continues to create innovative services for its customers, so it can remain competitive in the marketplace.

The innovation team asked their customer rep what he felt was working about the current system. He could only think of three items:

What's Working

1.	There is a strategic planning process already in place (but it's unclear if the strategic plan is realistic)
2.	Innovation projects with a senior leader champion are generally successful
3.	There is a support group—the Project Support Office—that intervenes when projects are in trouble

4. Ask the customer to define their problems with the current system, and then to rate the magnitude of each one. Have the customer describe the effect these problems have on the business.

What does the customer perceive to be the problem with the current system? What is the current system supposed to be able to do that it can't do now?

For each problem the customer identifies, ask why it's a problem. For each problem, ask the customer to rate, on a scale of 1 to 5, the severity of the problem;

> 1 = very minor problem
>
> 2 = minor problem
>
> 3 = moderate problem
>
> 4 = major problem
>
> 5 = very major problem

Having the customer talk about the impact these problems have on their business is the first step in moving the customer along the adoption process. The more severe the problems, the larger an innovation the customer will be willing to accept. If the problems are small, then it's less likely the customer will accept a radically new solution.

The innovation team worked with the sponsor to map out the perceived problems with the current innovation system:

Perceived Problems

Problems with the Innovation System	Why it's a problem	Rating
1. Innovation projects don't necessarily solve the problems that they were intended to solve	The problems still exist, which means the business hasn't moved forward	5
2. Innovations are mostly safe solutions—they are not breakthroughs	A lot of effort is expended for a small return	5
3. Innovation projects take too long or are never completed	Waste of resources	5
4. Projects require senior level championship to be successful	Waste of senior leaders' time	4
5. Not clear if the Project Support Office is being helpful to the process	Waste of resources	3
6. There is no way for the Executive Council to know how their strategy plan is progressing during the year	The strategic plan is not implemented and opportunities are missed	5
7. Project leaders don't push back when the customer requests a specific solution; therefore, more creative solutions aren't considered	Missed opportunities	4

●●●

5. Explore with the customer what they wish the system could do if anything were possible. Describe and then rate the impact each wish would have on the business if it were fulfilled.

- Have the customer complete the following statement, "Wouldn't it be nice if the system was able to. . ."

- For each "wouldn't it be nice" statement, have the customer first describe the impact on their business and then rate the level of impact on the same one-to-five scale used on page 42.

CASE STUDY

The innovation team worked with the customer representative, who in turn received inputs from the Executive Council, about what they wanted to see in a new system (see page 45).

The team felt uncertain about the ability of Operation Innovation to deliver on some of the items on the wish list but then reminded themselves that these were not requirements, just wishes; and although they would provide direction to the search for a solution, the team was not committed to delivering on the list. They were simply getting data on what an ideal system would look like for the customer.

New System Thoughts ⑤

Wouldn't it be nice	Impact on business	Rating
1. If there was a process that would ensure that the strategic plan was implemented each year	• The business would move forward more quickly • Senior leaders would be freed up to capture more opportunities for the business	5
2. If the majority of innovation projects were successful	Higher rate of innovation change	5
3. If everyone knew the status of all innovation projects at all times	Leaders would be able to take action before a project was in trouble and thus eliminate rework or project failure	3
4. If the solutions implemented were more creative and really moved the organization outside its current paradigm	Move the business forward more quickly	4
5. If the organization was more open to change	Innovations would be more successful because they would be adopted	5

• • •

6. Ask the customer to describe what the over-all impact to the business would be if no changes were made to the current system.

😊 This is another step in assessing what overall level of "pain" the customer is experiencing with the current system. What would happen if nothing changed? What impact would that have on the business?

> **CASE STUDY**
>
> If no changes were made to the current system, Longevity would continue to lag behind its competition in upgrading its services. This could be disastrous. The ability to innovate is key to staying competitive; not making a change was just not an acceptable option as far as the senior leaders were concerned.

7. Ask the customer to describe how their business is expected to change over the next five years.

😊 Aquire a sense of where the customer perceives their business will be in five years. Remember, you're not looking to just solve today's problems, but to capture opportunities that will help position the customer well in the future.

> **CASE STUDY**
>
> The team suggested the following expected changes in Longevity's business over the next five years:
>
> ❏ Continued cost pressure from insurance providers
>
> ❏ High expectations of customers for service
>
> *continued...*

❏ Continuing to adopt new medical technology to stay current with the rapidly changing field

❏ More consolidation of hospital systems

❏ More vertical integration of services

❏ Erosion of traditional hospital services through emergency clinics, in-office surgical services, etc.

8. Explore with the customer whether there is anything that could get in the way of their adopting a new solution.

Ask the customer, "If there was a solution that you could implement today that solved all of the problems with the current system and that satisfied your wish list, what obstacles might get in the way of getting it implemented?"

- This question brings to the surface any adoption issues the customer is aware of and willing to admit.

What kind of a track record does the customer have for adoption in the past? Understanding the customer's track record gives the team an idea of how receptive the customer is to change.

- How has the customer been successful at adopting solutions that had minor improvements? Major improvements? Have they adopted a completely reinvented system of any kind? A new invention?

- Ask the customer what kinds of adoption problems they experienced during those prior change efforts? What if anything is different about the current environment?

What leadership support does the customer have for the creation and implementation of a new solution? Is their leader on board? Is the customer's team on board?

The customer rep identified several major obstacles that would get in the way of implementing a new innovation system:

❑ Disruption to day-to-day operations

❑ Not enough resources allocated to get the system implemented

❑ Leadership resistance to another new initiative

❑ Leadership resistance by senior leaders to giving up vertical power in order to collaborate more cross-functionally

❑ Project manager resistance to changing their role to that of innovation leaders

❑ Resistance from project managers that their projects would be more visible

❑ Leadership and project managers lack skills when it comes to innovation. Lack of skills of leadership and project managers in innovation tools

●●●

---

9. Explore the resources available to the customer for creating a solution.

How much time is available for building a solution? Is there a deadline? What is the budget for the innovation?

(📝) Is the customer or customer representative willing to participate in the entire Innovation Process?

- How much effort can the customer expend during the innovation process? Can they dedicate representatives to the innovation team?

- Is the customer (if internal) willing to take ownership of the innovation project? If not, what level of involvement are they willing to take on? What accountability are they willing to accept?

> If the customer or the customer's representative is not willing to take ownership/accountability for the innovation project, then there is a high probability that the innovation will fail. The group with the highest stake in the outcome of the project should be the innovation owner and that should be the customer or the customer representative. The innovation team is there to support them.

TIP

CASE STUDY

The customer rep indicated that the team would work on Operation Innovation part time. The budget available to them would be $10k. They would have four months to come up with their recommendations for a solution. The customer rep took ownership/accountability for the project.

10. Determine the Type of Innovation that will be required to solve the customer's problem.

After assessing the customer's perceptions of the problem, the customer's "wouldn't it be nice" list, the level of pain experienced with the current system, and the resources available (including time), what Type of Innovation fits best?

> 1 = Minor improvement
>
> 2 = Major Improvement
>
> 3 = Reinvention
>
> 4 = Invention

CASE STUDY

The team debated on whether this was a Type 2, major improvement, or Type 3, reinvention project. Some elements of a system, such as strategic planning and project intervention, were already in place. However, so many elements were missing and would have to be created, that they decided that it was more like a Type 3 than a Type 2 innovation.

2 CAUSE ANALYSIS

Find the origins of the problem

The *Cause Analysis* tool is used to find the root causes of any problem. To determine if you need to do a cause analysis, consider the three scenarios below:

1) If the system is going to be improved, then the causes of the problem need to be investigated so they can be eliminated.

2) If the system is going to be reinvented, then there is no need to do a cause analysis because the original system with the problem will be replaced.

3) If the team is trying to find a long-term solution to a problem, then the causes of the problem should be investigated and corrected. (This is problem solving and is not an innovation because nothing new has been created. (For more on problem solving, see the *Creative Problem Solving* tool.)

Cause analysis starts with a description of the current problem (identified with the *Needs Assessment* tool) and then works backward in time to identify likely causes of the problem (first-level causes). Then it looks at what might have caused the causes (second-level causes), and it continues to look for causes until it reaches a dead end. When two or more branches end with the same cause, it is called a root cause, which is a fertile

---

target for innovation because its elimination or resolution will have multiple, positive results. For each potential cause identified, evidence is sought to confirm or deny that it is truly a cause of the problem.

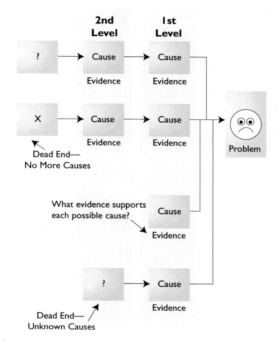

The Tree Structure of the Cause Analysis tool

The Innovation Tools Memory Jogger™ | ©2009 GOAL/QPC

Why do it?

🙂 To increase the customer's and sponsor's confidence that the team has identified the real sources of the problem.

🙂 For improvement projects, the customer will not want to adopt a solution that does not address the causes of the problems they are currently experiencing.

🙂 For invention and reinvention projects, where the current system will be completely replaced, a cause analysis is usually a waste of time. (The exception would be to identify causal factors that could be the source of problems for a new system as well.)

What does it do?

🙂 Builds a tree diagram that depicts ideas for causes, starting with the first level or direct causes of the problem and working back in time, showing causes of causes, until no more causes can be found.

🙂 Identifies any evidence/data to support the supposition that a cause actually produced an observed effect.

How do I do it?

✍ **1. Identify the problem to be investigated. Describe what is known about the problem.**

If the team did a Needs Assessment or if they are using the Creative Problem Solving tool, then they've already identified the problem to be solved. Move onto Step 2.

😊 What is the problem being experienced by the customer? What was expected from the system and what is being experienced now?

DEFINITION: A problem is a gap between what was expected and the current state.

😊 Where is the problem?

😊 How big is the problem?

😊 How frequent is the problem?

  😊 Is it a recurring problem? A one-time incident?

😊 Is the problem growing? If so, how quickly?

😊 What are the problem's boundaries? Where does it start and where does it end?

😊 Under what circumstances is there a problem? Under what circumstances is there no problem?

  😊 Are there instances when the system works as expected and no problem exists? What are these circumstances?

CASE STUDY

Champion Global Hotel in New York City, NY, prides itself on providing superior service in the luxury accommodation market. The clientele of the hotel was surveyed and it was found that fast room service delivery is highly valued by their high-end business guests. Champion Global assessed its delivery times for room service and found that the average length of time it takes to deliver an evening meal (between 6 p.m. and 9 p.m.) is 40 minutes. An innovation team was chartered to reduce the time of delivery.

They evaluated the problem. For at least the past six months, room service orders have taken an average of 40 minutes during the evening hours. The expectation is that the room service meal will be delivered in 30 minutes or less. The team set out to determine the causes of the room service delay.

✐ 2. Brainstorm possible first level causes.

For brainstorming guidelines see page 113 of the Idea Generation tool

DEFINITION: First-level causes are those that might have directly caused the problem. If you were to move back in time from the problem, these would be things that might have triggered the problem to occur.

- 😃 Ask, "Why did this problem occur?" Brainstorm answers, "Because . . ."
  - ✐ Record all ideas for causes on self-adhesive notes and then place first-level causes to the left of the problem statement, in the first branch of a tree diagram (built from right to left)

The team brainstormed first-level causes of the room service delivery problem and drew the tree diagram shown on page 56.

1st Level Causes

Orders aren't entered into the computer immediately

Orders take too long to prepare by chefs

Wait staff doesn't prepare room trays ahead of time

Food is not delivered immediately when prepared

Food takes too long to deliver to room

Why? Because...

Problem

Room service orders take 40 minutes during evening dinner hours

3. Brainstorm potential second-level causes.

DEFINITION: A second level cause is one that could directly result in a first-level cause.

- Ask the question, "What could have caused each first-level cause to occur?"

- Record each possible second-level cause on a self-adhesive note and place it on the second-level branch of the tree diagram, to the left of the first-level cause with which it is associated.

  - Each level of the tree represents events that occurred further back in time.

- Continue to build tree branches (third- and even fourth-level causes) until the team hits a point of ignorance or a dead end.

  - Ignorance = there is no more information available, mark with a "?"

  - Dead end = the end of a chain of causation; nothing else happened. There are no more causes. Mark with an "X."

Here is what a portion of the team's completed tree diagram looked like:

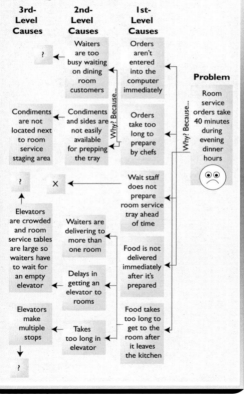

✐ 4. Identify any evidence (data) associated with each of the brainstormed causes.

😊 On another self-adhesive note, capture any evidence that indicates that the cause could have contributed to the problem.

    ⊚ Evidence should be factual or observable. Evidence does not include assumptions about motivation or psychological states. It doesn't include anything that can't be observed directly.

CASE STUDY

The team searched for evidence that backed up their brainstormed causes. They

> Condiments are not located next to room service staging area

> **Evidence:** The elements (other than food) needed for the room service table are located in various sections of the kitchen

> Elevators are crowded & room service tables are large so waiters have to wait for an empty elevator

> **Evidence:** It takes an average of 10 minutes to get an elevator during peak dinner hours

looked at the idea that the elements (other than the food prep) needed to prepare the room service tray were not all in one place. After surveying the kitchen, they found this idea to be true. Condiments are in one area, silverware and napkins in another, coffee/tea in another. They also sought evidence to confirm that waiters couldn't get on the elevators because they were crowded and the room service rolling tables were too large to fit. They spoke with room service personnel who did confirm this problem. They then collected data on how long, on average, it took to get an elevator and found that it took 10 minutes.

✐ 5. Determine which causes are the primary causes of the problem. Write a cause statement.

😃 Based on the evidence collected, what hypothesis does the team have about what caused the problem?

  😊 Keep in mind that there are typically multiple causes for any one problem (or multiple causes for any one effect). Therefore, the team isn't necessarily looking for a single cause. Instead, it's looking for the multiple causes, which together, caused the problem

😃 Determine how the team can test their hypothesis.

  😊 Brainstorm ways that the team can test the potential causes in order to generate evidence that supports one way or the other.

    😊 Is there a way to run the system without the causes to see if the problem goes away?

Use the Factorial Design of Experiments tool to test hypotheses about causes.

😃 Write a statement that explains the causes of the problem.

  😊 Attach the evidence to support the cause statement

The evidence that the team collected on causes indicated there were three significant causes of delays:

1) taking too long to prepare the room service tray because the supplies for the table were not located in the kitchen,

2) the size of the room service rolling tables and the crowdedness of the elevators during peak evening hours, which resulted in a 10-minute-delay, and

3) room service waiters attending to dining room customers when the room service order was ready, which could create a delay in delivery from 5 to 15 minutes.

With the causes identified, the team could begin to design a solution to the problem.

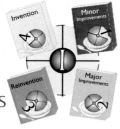

3 FACTORIAL DESIGN OF EXPERIMENTS

Test three factors in one experiment

The *Factorial Design of Experiments* tool helps a team design and conduct experiments to test their hypotheses. It analyzes the influence of two or more factors on a response (or responses) of interest.

In this *Factorial Design of Experiments* tool, we examine a 2^3 factorial design, which is a way to test the effects of three different factors, at two different levels each—a high level and a low level—on a response or result of interest. Each factor is assessed individually (A, B, C) and then in combination with the other factors (AB, BC, AC, and ABC), enabling the experimenter to study both the effects of the individual factors and the interactions between them.

Once you've learned to do a three-factor factorial, you can easily extend it to four factors or roll it back to two.

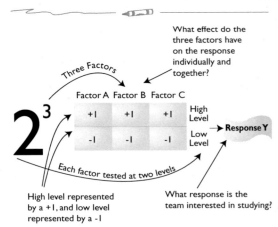

What effect do the three factors have on the response individually and together?

Three Factors

Factor A Factor B Factor C

| +1 | +1 | +1 | High Level |
| -1 | -1 | -1 | Low Level |

2^3

→ Response Y

Each factor tested at two levels

High level represented by a +1, and low level represented by a -1

What response is the team interested in studying?

The Elements of a Factorial Design of Experiment

Why do it?

- To test whether causes, assumptions, and hypotheses are true.

- To quickly screen a number of variables to see what effects they have on an outcome (response).

What does it do?

- Tests the individual and combined effects of three separate factors or variables, at two different levels each, on a response of interest. Determines if any of the effects are significant.

- Determines if there are any interactions of significance between the factors.

How do I do it?

✍ 1. Determine the Response (Y) to be measured

DEFINITION: The response is the outcome or result you are concerned about.

☺ What is the outcome of interest?

✍ 2. Determine the factors to be measured

DEFINITION: A factor is a variable that the team thinks might have an effect on the response.

☺ What are the three factors or variables the team wants to test? Label the first factor as "A," the second factor as "B," and the third as "C".

CASE STUDY

A team at the Champion Bread Company is studying the effect of two new brands of yeast on the height of whole wheat bread after it has been baked. Therefore, the Response (Y) to be measured will be the height of the bread in centimeters. Since yeast, Factor A, is sensitive to both sugar and gluten, the team has chosen to test two different levels of sugar, Factor B, and two different levels of gluten, Factor C.

✍ 3. Determine the two levels to be tested for each factor. Then code the low value as a "-1" and the high value as a "+1."

☺ Each factor will be tested at a high and a low level. The high and low levels can be whatever you choose, but it's a good idea to test what you think will be the upper and lower limits of the factor. The levels can also be qualitative, such as two types of an ingredient.

For purposes of calculation, we will use a coded value (-1 or +1) in place of the actual levels of each factor. So, every low level is coded as a -1 and every high level is coded as a +1.

The team tested yeast brands P and Q and they decided to make Brand P the "low level" and Brand Q the "high level." Therefore the coded value for Brand P was -1 and for Brand Q was +1. For sugar, they used the upper and lower limits of the amount of sugar typically used for baking bread: 2 teaspoons (tsp) for the high or +1 value and 1/2 a teaspoon for the low limit (-1). The two gluten levels were 1 tablespoon (tbs) and 3 tbs.

Factor	Factor Designation	Low Value	Coded Value for Low	High Value	Coded Value for High
Yeast	A	Brand P	-1	Brand Q	+1
Sugar	B	1/2 tsp	-1	2 tsp	+1
Gluten	C	1 tbs	-1	3 tbsp	+1

4. Calculate the number of experimental runs that will be required and set up a factorial table.

DEFINITION: A run is a single test of the overall experiment that includes a unique combination of the factors.

DEFINITION: A factorial table is a table used to record the levels of the factors to be tested in each run and the response measured at the end of the run.

⊛ The number of runs is simply two to the "k" power, where "k" is the number of factors. Since we are discussing a 2^3 factorial, the number of runs is two cubed or eight. (If you had four factors, then it would be twenty-four—two to the fourth power—or sixteen runs.) To create a factorial table see below.

　⊛ Each run tests a unique combination of levels of factors A, B, and C. So, in run #1, we test the low value of A, the low value of B, and the low value of C. With the eight runs we are able to test all the unique combinations of A, B and C

⊛ The column marked "Response Y" is left blank, and will be filled in in Step 5.

Factorial Table: +1 and -1 are called Coded Values. Instead of using actual levels, coded values are used as they facilitate analysis of the results.

Run #	Factor A = Yeast	Factor B = Sugar	Factor C = Gluten	Response Y (in cm)
1	-1	-1	-1	
2	+1	-1	-1	
3	-1	+1	-1	
4	+1	+1	-1	
5	-1	-1	+1	
6	+1	-1	+1	
7	-1	+1	+1	
8	+1	+1	+1	

✐ **5. Randomize the runs and then run each experiment and record the response data.**

DEFINITION: To randomize is to order something without purpose or design.

- To "randomize the runs" means the team will perform the experiments out of order, as a random sequence of runs.

  - Randomization reduces the influence of extraneous factors that the team is unaware of that influence the results

    - In the case study example of testing for bread height, a faulty oven thermostat that causes temperature to rise throughout the day would be an example of an extraneous factor.

- To generate a random sequence, simply write each of the run numbers on a slip of paper, fold it up, put it in a hat, shake it up, and then draw the slips of paper from the hat, writing down the run number as it's drawn. That's randomization! Or you can use a random number generator, but the hat is more fun!

Run #	Factor A = Yeast	Factor B = Sugar	Factor C = Gluten	Response Y (in cm)
1	-1	-1	-1	5
2	1	-1	-1	4
3	-1	1	-1	6
4	1	1	-1	9
5	-1	-1	1	10
6	1	-1	1	11
7	-1	1	1	14
8	1	1	1	13

(☺) If you look at the factorial table, it tells you which levels of each factor to test in run #1. In the case study example, for run #1 A is run at the low level = low yeast or Brand P; B is run at the low level = low sugar or ½ tsp; and C is run at the low level = low gluten or 1 tbsp.

(☺) After each run, record the response data in the "Response Y" column.

✐ 6. Analyze the main effects

DEFINITION: A main effect is the effect that any one of the single factors has on Response Y.

(☺) To measure the main response for factor B:

   (☺) Add all the High Level (+1) responses together and divide by 4 to get an average for the high level responses

   (☺) Add all the Low Level (-1) responses together and divide by 4 to get an average for the low level responses

   (☺) The average at the High Level minus the average at the Low Level = Effect

---

CASE STUDY

The team looked at the results for Factor B, sugar. At the high level (2 tsp of sugar), the average height was (6+9+14+13)/4 = 10.5. At the low level (1/2 teaspoon of sugar), the average height of the bread (the response) was (5+4+10+11)/4 = 7.5 cm. (See table on page 68.)

Thus the (main) effect of Factor B, i.e., of changing from the high level (+1) to the low level (-1), on

continued...

---

the height of the bread was the difference between the two or 10.5 −7.5 = 3. In other words, loaves made with 2 tsp of sugar are on average 3 cm higher than those made with ½ tsp sugar.

Run #	Factor B = Sugar	Response Y (in cm)
1	-1	5
2	1	4
3	-1	6
4	1	9
5	-1	10
6	1	11
7	-1	14
8	1	13
Average at High Level:		10.5
Average at Low Level:		7.5
Effect:		3

Do the same calculations for Factors A and C.

Set your factorial table up in a spreadsheet to make the calculations of the averages and effects faster and easier. Or, there are software programs, such as Minitab™ or JMP™ that will do all the calculations for you.

TIP

✐ 7. Analyze the interaction effects

> **DEFINTION:** An interaction is a synergistic or antagonistic effect between two or more factors.

☺ In our example, the possible interactions are AB, BC, AC, and ABC.

☺ To calculate the BC interaction:

   ✐ Add all the responses from High Levels (+1) of the BC combination and divide by 4. In our example, the average of all the high-level response values is 9.

   ✐ Add all the responses from Low Levels (-1) of the BC combination and divide by 4. The average of all the low-level response values, in our example, is also 9.

   ✐ The BC interaction effect is the difference between the average of the high levels and the average of the low levels. In our example, the effect is a zero.

CASE STUDY

The team calculated the average of the high level to be 9 and the average of the low level also to be 9, which resulted in an effect of zero. That meant that there was no interaction between the factors sugar and gluten on the height of the bread.

continued...

Run #	Factor B = Sugar	Factor C = Gluten	Interaction BC Coded Value	Response Y (in cm)
1	-1	+1	-1	5
2	-1	+1	-1	4
3	+1	+1	+1	6
4	+1	+1	+1	9
5	-1	-1	+1	10
6	-1	-1	+1	11
7	+1	-1	-1	14
8	+1	-1	-1	13
Average at High Level:				9
Average at Low Level:				9
Effect:				0

Do the same calculations for the interactions of AB, AC, and ABC.

The results for all the main responses and interactions for the team's experiment are shown below. (The numbers with a "-" in front of them are the low values. The numbers with a "+" in front of them are the high values.)

continued...

	A	B	C	AB	BC	AC	ABC
	-5	-5	-5	+5	+5	+5	-5
	+4	-4	-4	-4	+4	-4	+4
	-6	+6	-6	-6	-6	+6	+6
	+9	+9	-9	+9	-9	-9	-9
	-10	-10	+10	+10	-10	-10	+10
	+11	-11	+11	+11	-11	+11	-11
	-14	-14	+14	-14	+14	-14	-14
	+13	+13	+13	+13	+13	+13	+13
High Level:	9.25	10.5	12	9.25	9	8.75	8.25
Low Level:	8.75	7.5	6	8.75	9	9.25	9.75
Effect Value:	0.5	3	6	0.5	0	-0.5	-1.5

8. Rank the effects from lowest to highest and assign a ranking number to each.

Sort the effect values from lowest to the highest. Assign a rank to each, starting with the lowest as a rank of 1, moving up to the highest as a rank of 7.

The team sorted their results, beginning with the lowest effect result of -1.5 for the ABC interaction and gave that a rank of 1. The next lowest was -0.5 and that got a rank of 2.

Effect	Value	Rank
ABC	-1.5	1
AC	-0.5	2
BC	0	3
A	0.5	4
AB	0.5	5
B	3	6
C	6	7

9. Calculate the Z-Value score for each effect

DEFINITION: A Z-Value score is a calculated statistical number that is used to determine the significance of each effect.

To get the Z-Value score, you need to first calculate a probability rating using the formula:

- Probability = (Rank Value (RV) minus 0.5) divided by (# Runs minus 1)

$$\text{Probability} = \frac{RV - 0.05}{\#Runs - 1}$$

- So, for our example, the BC probability would be calculated as follows:

  (3-0.5) divided by (8-1) = 0.357

Calculating the Z-Value score requires a normal distribution table or a spreadsheet program.

- Enter the following formula in each Z-Value cell: "=NORMINV(cell # for the probability value for the effect in question,0,1)"

- So, let's say the Probability value of ABC (0.071) was in cell D2, then the formula would be: =NORMINV(D2,0,1)

The team calculated the probability values and then set up a spreadsheet to calculate the Z-Values.

	A	B	C	D	E
1	Factor	Effect	Rank	Probability	Z Value
2	ABC	-1.5	1	0.071	-1.465
3	AC	-0.5	2	0.214	-0.792
4	BC	0	3	0.357	-0.366
5	A	0.5	4	0.500	0.000
6	AB	0.5	5	0.786	0.792
7	B	3	6	0.643	0.366
8	C	6	7	0.929	1.465

Formula in this cell (E5) was: =NORMINV (D5,0,1)

✍ 10. Plot the Z-Value score against the Effect Value

☝ Draw a plot with the Effect Value on the x-axis and the Z-Value on the y-axis.

☝ Plot each of the 7 points.

☝ Draw in a straight line that appears to provide a good fit to the majority of the points.

☝ If all the plotted points are close to being on a straight line, you can conclude that the factors did not influence the response. Points that are "out of line" indicate "real" effects.

The team drew their plot and noted that five of the points formed a straight line but two, B (Factor B) and C (Factor C), were outside the line, which meant the amount of sugar and gluten added to the bread did influence height. But that was something the team already knew. Factor A was on the line so they deduced that brand of yeast did not have an effect on the height, and that the interactions involving Factor A (AB, AC and ABC) were also not significant because they were also on the straight line.

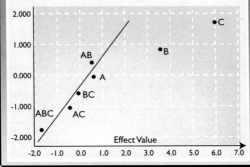

Check with your patent attorney for recommendations on how to record data for patent purposes.

4 PARADIGM DECON- STRUCTION

Drill down to the assumptions

A paradigm, broadly speaking, describes a mental model for a segment of reality, which is separated from other segments by a set of paradigm boundaries. For example, if we were to examine the paradigm of a book, the paradigm boundaries might include bound books but not binders or refillable books. Boundaries tell us what is inside and outside the paradigm we're examining. Within the boundaries are a set of concepts that describe the paradigm, such as a book is made out of paper that is bound together with a front and back cover. The paradigm concepts are supported by rules that tell the user of the paradigm what can and cannot be done within that segment of reality. "A book cannot be less than 50 pages in length" would be a rule. "A book must be made of paper" would be another rule.

Supporting these concepts and rules are assumptions. Assumptions are, beliefs that we consider to be true. Some beliefs are based on evidence; some are not. An assumption for a book might be that books exist to provide entertainment or learning.

Finally, with any paradigm there are problems that it does not solve, because those problems don't fit into the existing mental model—they don't fit with the concepts, they break the rules, or they don't comply with the assumptions. These unsolved problems are clues to a new paradigm—one that can be explored with the *Paradigm Construction* tool.

Elements of a Deconstructed Paradigm

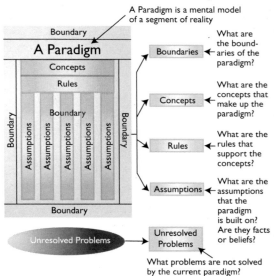

A Paradigm is a mental model of a segment of reality

Boundaries ← What are the boundaries of the paradigm?

Concepts ← What are the concepts that make up the paradigm?

Rules ← What are the rules that support the concepts?

Assumptions ← What are the assumptions that the paradigm is built on? Are they facts or beliefs?

Unresolved Problems ← What problems are not solved by the current paradigm?

Why do it?

(☺) Whether the team is endeavoring to invent a new system or reinvent the existing one, it's useful to know the concepts, rules, and assumptions that were used to form the current system. Then the team can construct new assumptions and rules in order to build a new paradigm (using, of course, the *Paradigm Construction* tool).

What does it do?

- Helps the team to excavate the elements of the current paradigm so they can create a truly innovative – new solution.

- Identifies problems that the existing paradigm doesn't solve, which present opportunities for designing a new paradigm that will solve them.

How do I do it?

✎ 1. Name the paradigm to be deconstructed and then define the boundaries of the paradigm

- What is the segment of reality (area of technology, product, service, process, system) that is of interest?

- What is included in this segment? What is inside the boundaries of the segment?

- What is excluded? What is outside the boundaries of the segment?

> Detecting the elements of a paradigm, such as its boundaries, concepts (step 2), rules (step 3), assumptions (step 4), and unsolved problems (step 5) is very difficult to do. Don't expect to complete this task in one sitting. Go through the steps as best you can and observe the paradigm in action for awhile, study how it operates, then come back and take another pass at it. (See Chapter 4 for an explanation of why paradigms are so difficult to detect.)

In the early 1970s an innovation team was pulled together to explore the possibility of creating a whole new paradigm of how their newly formed company, ABC Airlines, could compete in the airline industry. They decided the first thing they needed to do was deconstruct the existing paradigm of commercial airline passenger service.

They defined the boundaries of the paradigm they were going to deconstruct as:

❑ Includes the "flight selection" experience for the passenger, including booking the flight, making changes to existing itineraries.

❑ Includes the "on the ground" experience of the passenger, including boarding and deplaning the aircraft, and the entire terminal experience, including gate-agent service, baggage checking, and handling and pick-up.

❑ Includes the routes the planes fly, including schedules and frequency of popular routes, number of stops and connections, and the overall elapsed time for travel from an initiating airport to a final destination.

❑ Includes the "on the plane" experience, including seating, physical comfort services (e.g., seat size and comfort, beverage and meal services, and any other amenities such as bathrooms, pillows, blankets).

❑ Includes the pricing of flights and the customer impression of the value delivered for the cost.

•••

2. Define the main concepts of the paradigm in question

> DEFINITION: Concepts are the primary descriptors or characteristics of the paradigm.

If you had to describe what the key concepts of the paradigm were, what would you say?

The team identified the following concepts as critical to the existing airline paradigm:

❑ Each type of plane has a certain seat capacity. The actual number of seats depends on the amount of space designated per seat.

❑ Each seat is inventoried as a unique space on each flight and sold in advance of the flight via ticketing programs.

Seats are arranged in "classes" of service (i.e., first, business, or economy class).

❑ Typically there are aisle, variable numbers of middle seats (sometimes none), and window seats.

❑ Aisle and window seats are preferred over middle seats.

❑ Pricing algorithms for seats are complex. There are pricing structures based on how far in advance before the flight a ticket is purchased (the closer to flight time, the more expensive). There are pricing differences by class of service (first class, business, economy). There are pricing differences based on the ability of the customer to switch flight plans. *continued...*

❑ Routes are organized around "hubs" where airlines concentrate their routes for competitive and cost advantages. Most flights route through one or more hubs, to consolidate passengers for feeder routes (spokes off the hub) from the hub to "secondary" markets.

❑ Hubs are typically located in large cities that are attractive to business and nonbusiness travelers.

❑ Competitive dominance is obtained by dominating gates at airports using the hub-and-spoke model.

●●●

✍ 3. Write the rulebook for the paradigm.

☺ A paradigm is like a game, and so, like a game, it has a set of rules that the players (the people who are involved in the paradigm) live by.

TIP

For example, if you sat down to watch a game of rugby and had no idea how the game was played, all you would see was the action on the field. As you continued to watch, however, you'd slowly begin to guess what the rules were. That is what you must do with the paradigm you're studying: Detect the rules that underlie the game.

☺ Concepts exist because there are a set of rules that cause the concepts to come to life.

☺ Brainstorm the rules by asking, "What are the underlying rules that define this paradigm?"

- Rules generally sound something like this: "You must . . ."; "If x happens, then y must occur"; "You cannot do z . . . ."

- Rules tend to be black and white, such as "There can only be 11 players on the field at one time."

- The rules are the definition of how the paradigm operates.

CASE STUDY

The team spent some time considering what the rules of the game were for the airline passenger business and came up with a rulebook for the airline industry paradigm:

❑ There must be different classes of service (at least first class and coach).

❑ The airline must focus on business travelers as they are the basis of profitability.

❑ Business travelers require special treatment such as seating class upgrades.

❑ An airline must provide a reward program (loyalty program) that is based on miles flown and which rewards passengers with free flights, upgrades, etc.

❑ Seats must be assigned either at ticketing or at flight check-in.

❑ Airlines must use a hub-and-spoke system to maximize flight loads.

❑ Meals must be served on all flights longer than 2 hours.

continued...

❑ Free nonalcoholic beverages (soda, coffee, etc.) and snacks must be served on all flights longer than one hour. Alcoholic beverages must be offered free in first and business classes, and offered for sale in coach class.

❑ Airlines must not compete on price if they want to be profitable.

❑ Planes must fly at full capacity to fully profit.

✍ **4. Dig down deeper to discover any assumptions associated with the identified concepts and rules. Identify the evidence to support each assumption.**

☺ In order to get to the assumptions, take each concept or rule and ask "why" over and over again until you get to the basic assumptions.

☺ You can tell basic assumptions by: facts that can be verified or not, or statements such as, "that's just the way it is," or "this is how it has to work," or "it's always been this way."

☺ Beliefs are not based on evidence and are therefore the biggest levers for reinventing the paradigm. (See *Paradigm Construction* tool.)

  ◌ Example of a belief: Children should learn to read by the end of the first-grade.

  ◌ Example of a fact: Sally is able to read a first-grade primer.

- ☺ Projecting into the future is an assumption. All or nothing words are assumptions.

☺ Most things we think of as facts are really beliefs. Facts are accepted as self-evident, requiring no further proof.

- ☺ It used to be a "fact" that the sun revolved around the Earth. Was that really a fact? No, it was an assumption dressed up as a fact. Our current scientific "facts" are likewise mostly assumptions or, in scientific parlance, they are called theories, which are often treated like un-changeable facts. In truth, they are beliefs sup-ported by some evidence that's true only within the paradigm itself. True facts never change.

☺ For each assumption ask, "What evidence is there to support it?"

Digging down to discover the assumptions

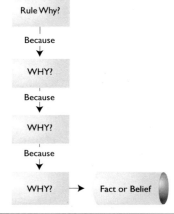

The team drilled down to the assumptions behind each rule and found the following assumptions for the rule "Seats must be assigned either at ticketing or at flight check-in":

Why must seats be assigned either at ticketing or at flight check-in?

❑ Customers want to choose where to sit. Why?

   ❑ Not all seats are considered desirable; middle seats are the least desirable.

   ❑ Evidence supports that middle seats sell last and, therefore, are the least desirable, but it's only true within the existing paradigm. If middle seats were twice the size of aisle/window seats, they might be more desirable.

Why must seats be assigned either at ticketing or at flight check-in?

❑ It motivates customers to book reservations earlier to ensure they get what they consider a "good" seat. Why?

   ❑ Within the existing model, the more desirable seats sell out sooner. There is evidence to support this within the existing paradigm.

❑ Without assigned seating the boarding process is chaos. Why would there be chaos if seats aren't assigned?

   ❑ No one would know where to sit and everyone would fight over the desirable seats. This is a belief, not a fact.

- 😊 Unsolved problems are things the paradigm can't do, or that the paradigm can't explain.

  - 😊 For example, a spontaneous remission of an incurable disease is an unsolved problem of the medical paradigm. There is no medical explanation for the phenomenon. But that doesn't necessarily mean the phenomenon isn't real. It means that the paradigm boundaries, concepts, rules, and assumptions do not cover that phenomenon. It signifies an opportunity to change the paradigm because there is a phenomenon that doesn't fit the existing mental model.

- 😊 Unsolved problems are difficult to identify because we live in our existing paradigms and believe the assumptions supporting them to be true and that the things that they can't do are either not real or just the way it is. These are seductions of the existing paradigm that we must ruthlessly resist if we are to be true innovators.

CASE STUDY

The team struggled to come up with unsolved problems of the airline industry, spent some time observing what didn't work, and came up with a list of unsolved problems or unfulfilled needs:

❏ It's hard to sell middle seats, particularly on long flights.

❏ Business travelers desire more flexibility in changing their flying plans because business plans often change at the last minute.

continued...

Travel times are long if the traveler is traveling between non-hub city airports (between secondary markets).

Business customers prefer to carry on their luggage rather than check it. Many of the bags they want to carry on will not fit in the existing overhead bins, which slows the boarding process and frustrates the business traveler.

Business customers frequently delay their boarding in hopes of obtaining a last-minute upgrade in class service, slowing the boarding process.

At times, the same specific seat is assigned to two different passengers, which is not discovered until the boarding process. This can delay flight departures.

•••

6. Have the paradigm definition validated by others.

Review your paradigm boundaries, concepts, rules, assumptions, and evidence with the customer (or customer reps), technical experts, stakeholders, as well as people from outside the system to see if you've captured all that is known about the paradigm.

Use the Paradigm Construction tool to build a new paradigm.

5 CONTEXT DIAGRAM

Identifying the stakeholders

The *Context Diagram* is used to visualize the interfaces of either: a) the current system, or b) a new solution. With it, the team can identify each group, system and

The Elements of a Context Diagram

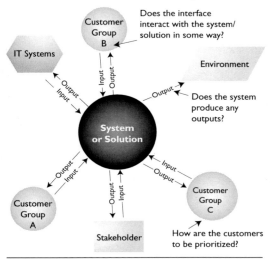

Does the interface interact with the system/solution in some way?

Does the system produce any outputs?

How are the customers to be prioritized?

environment that the system or solution will interact with, also known as stakeholders. The outputs from the system or solution to the stakeholder are labeled, as are the inputs from the stakeholders to the system/solution.

The current system is usually diagrammed in the early stages of the innovation process to ensure that system stakeholders are identified and can be included in the innovation project. Later on, after the potential solutions are reduced to the two to four real contenders, the team may want to generate a *Context Diagram* for each, to help them identify the stakeholders of each potential solution. This information can help the team define the appropriate team participation in the development stage for the solution that is eventually selected.

Why do it?

(☺) Identifies stakeholders in order to include them in the innovation process. Participation, either as a team member or by providing input through a team member liaison, helps to build buy-in and commitment to the innovation process.

(☺) When there is more than one customer group, the customer groups need to be prioritized so the team will know how their various needs, criteria for selection, and desired characteristics for the final solution, should be prioritized.

What does it do?

(☺) Identifies the stakeholders, the inputs from the system/solution to the stakeholders, and the outputs from the system back out to the stakeholders.

(🖉) Identifies stakeholder representatives.

(🖉) When there are multiple customer groups, creates a prioritized list of customers.

How do I do it?

✐ 1. Identify the system to be mapped.

(🖉) Write the name of the system (product, service, process, system) in the middle of a circle.

(🖉) If the team is mapping a potential solution, substitute the word "system" with the word "solution."

✐ 2. Define any outputs produced by the system.

DEFINITION: An output is the result of a series of steps within a process.

(🖉) An output can be something tangible, like a product, or intangible, like data.

> If the existing system is a product, then it probably doesn't produce any outputs.
>
> If the existing system is a process, then its outputs are the product(s) it produces as well as any byproducts (wastes).

TIP

✐ 3. Identify the groups, systems, and environments that will receive the outputs or that interface with the system in any way.

(🖉) Look at the external interfaces from the point of view of the system itself. If you were the system:

- What customer and user groups do you interface with? (Draw these as circles.)

- What stakeholders do you interface with? (Draw these as squares.)

- What systems (such as IT systems) do you interface with? (Draw these as hexagrams.)

- What components of the environment do you interface with? (Draw these as parallelograms.)

- If the system produces an output to an external interface, draw an arrow from the system to the external interface and label the arrow with the name of the output.

4. Identify the inputs between the system and its interfaces.

- Identify any inputs from the interface groups to the system.

  - Draw an arrow from the external interface to the system to represent an input to the system.

  - Write the name of the input on the line.

CASE STUDY

Bilbo Banks, a small national commercial bank ($10 billion in assets), had carved out a very profitable niche by focusing on lending to high-tech start-up companies that originally had been funded by venture capitalists. The bank is now seeing increased competition from un-regulated financial companies (especially leasing and insurance firms) that do not have the same regulatory requirements for documentation and credit-worthiness of debtors. *continued...*

The bank assembled an innovation team to devise a solution to the problem of unregulated lenders. The team came up with several possible solutions, one of which they called the SuperSonic Loan Program. It would provide an expedited loan process for their high-tech market. The team then developed the following *context diagram* of the inputs and outputs from each group that would interface with the program:

5. Identify a representative for each stakeholder.

If the team is mapping several potential solutions, then skip this step. After the final solution has been selected (Solution Selection tool), go back and complete this step (select representatives from each interface group).

☺ Each interface group is a stakeholder in the innovation effort.

☺ The team will need to solicit a representative from each stakeholder to either sit on the team (if it's a key stakeholder) or to liaise with the innovation team.

　☺ Stakeholders who do not sit on the innovation team should have access to a team member who acts as a liaison to the stakeholder group. This liaison collects inputs from the stakeholder and provides communications back to the stakeholder about what is happening with the project.

✎ 6. If there is more than one customer group, create a prioritized list of customers.

☺ You'll need to work with your innovation team leader or the sponsor to determine how to prioritize the customer groups. Which is most important? Which group is next in importance?

It's critical that the team prioritize the customer groups so that if there are conflicts between the needs of the groups, the team will know which set of needs, criteria, desired characteristics, and performance goals is the highest priority and then the next highest, etc. Record the rationale or criteria used for prioritization, so that if conditions change, the prioritization can be revisited.

6 SOLUTION CRITERIA & DESIRED CHARACTERISTICS (DC) PRIORITIZATION

Discovering solution criteria and desired characteristics

In Part I of the *Solution Criteria & Desired Characteristics (DC) Prioritization* tool, the criteria for selecting the best possible solution are elicited from the customer and sorted into Go/No Go versus Weighted criteria. In Part Two, the desired characteristics (DCs) of the final solution are defined by the customer, who then rates the importance of each to the business. In addition, each desired characteristic is also rated by the customer for current performance, and for comparison of performance of the current system to a competitor or benchmarked system. A performance goal for each DC is also defined by the customer.

With this tool, the team is not committing to producing a solution with the DCs or performance goals defined by the customer, but instead is collecting data related to the vision the customer has for a final solution. (The team began the process of creating the bones of the customer's vision of a solution with

---

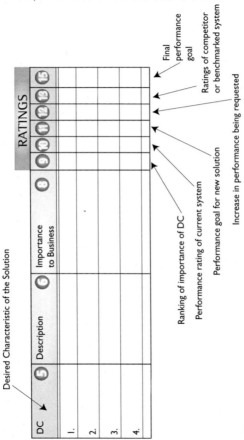

Desired Characteristic of the Solution

DC	Description	Importance to Business	RATINGS							
5	**6**	**7**	**8**	**9**	**10**	**11**	**12**	**13**	**15**
1.										
2.										
3.										
4.										

Final performance goal

Ratings of competitor or benchmarked system

Increase in performance being requested

Performance goal for new solution

Performance rating of current system

Ranking of importance of DC

the Needs Assessment tool. Now the team is adding some meat to those bones. The ultimate vision will be spelled out with the Vision Decomposition tool.) The Solution Criteria & DC Prioritization tool provides direction for the innovation effort without rigidly defining a prescription for a solution which would narrow the boundaries too early. The output of the tool is a Desired Characteristics Table.

Why do it?

- Involves the customer in a process of articulating, in relatively broad terms, what they want out of a final solution without creating a list of specific requirements. This allows the team to be more creative in designing options for solutions (Solution Synthesis tool).

What does it do?

- The team helps the customer develop a set of criteria that will be used to: a) filter the synthesized solutions and then b) select the final solution. (Part 1)

- The team helps the customer develop a list of desired characteristics (DCs), which are then prioritized into categories of "must haves," "strongly desired," and "nice to have" so that the team has an idea of what is most important to the customer and what they might be able to negotiate when it comes to designing a final solution. (Part 2)

- Develops the customer's performance goals for each of the desired characteristics. (Part 2)

- Compares the current system to a competitor or benchmarked system. (Part 3)

Defines what resources will be available to develop a solution. (Part 4)

How do I do it?

Part 1—Defining criteria for selection

✎ **1. Have the customer brainstorm the criteria they would like the team to use to select the best possible solution.**

- Refer to the rules of brainstorming on page 113.

  DEFINITION: Solution criteria are used to make decisions about which solution should be selected for development.

- Collect solution criteria from the customer, from all key stakeholders, and from the sponsor (who is the provider of the organization's criteria).

  - Organizational criteria address the needs of the organization, such as criteria around what the budget for development/implementation can be, the type of resources that can be utilized, and the type of technology to be included.

- To collect information from the stakeholders and sponsor, follow the steps in Part 1 and just substitute the name "Stakeholder" or "Sponsor" for the word "Customer."

- Write each idea for a criterion on a self-adhesive note and place it on a flipchart page.

✍ 2. After all the ideas for criteria have been generated, ask the customer to select the top ten criteria.

😊 There don't have to be exactly ten criteria. The criteria will be used to focus on what is most important to the customer when selecting a solution. Limiting the criteria to ten to begin with forces the customer to focus on the most important elements that the team should use deciding which solution option fits best with what the customer wants out of a solution.

✍ 3. Separate the top ten criteria into the two categories: "Go/No Go" and "Weighted," then add additional criteria to the Weighted group to bring it back up to a total of ten Weighted criteria.

😊 A Go/No Go criterion is one that if the solution doesn't meet it, the solution is discarded and will not be considered further. Therefore, it's important that the customer is careful about choosing Go/No Go criteria.

- 😊 Make sure the Go/No Go criteria are written so a "yes" response = GO and a "no" response = NO GO.

- 😊 Because any Go/No Go criterion can eliminate a solution, each one must be very important to the customer. As a result, all Go/No Go criteria are of equal importance, as any one of them can eliminate a potential solution being considered for development.

- 😊 The list of Go/No Go criteria is usually shorter than the list of Weighted criteria.

😊 A Weighted criterion is one that the solution can partially meet and still stay in the game.

- Some Weighted criteria are more important than others, which is why they will be given relative weights (in Step 4) as indicators of their relative importance to the customer.

4. Ask the customer (or stakeholder) to assign a weight to each of the ten Weighted criteria on a scale of 1 to 10.

- The weight indicates the importance to the customer of a criterion.

  - A "1" weight means the criterion is extremely unimportant.

  - A "5" means the criterion is moderately important.

  - A "10" weight means the criterion is extremely important.

  - Based on the scale above, a weight of "8" would mean a very important criterion. A weight of "3" would mean very unimportant.

It's not likely that the team will have criteria that are rated a "1" or "2" in the final list of ten weighted criteria. If they do, they should go back and see if there aren't other, more important, criteria to substitute.

TIP

It's 1980 and the XYZ company that has been successful in providing the expedited delivery of packages for its primary customers, large computer companies, is now assessing how to expand this same service to serve a larger market segment and to add the overnight delivery of documents, particularly for the financial services market. Before they do this, Client Services (CS) requested that an innovation project team design a new package tracking system. CS is accountable for tracking lost packages and responding to customer complaints. They currently have no way of knowing where in the XYZ system a package is located; they find out about a problem only after the client calls to complain. The innovation team, which includes representatives from CS as well as key stakeholder groups including accounting, planning, marketing/sales, information technology, air transport, and ground delivery, is working with CS to define solution criteria.

CS is particularly interested in creating a system that provides data which verify the route and timing of any specific package delivery in real-time. They believe such a system would help them respond to clients proactively, and enable them to pinpoint and eliminate problem areas, thus resulting in higher levels of customer satisfaction.

After identifying the top ten criteria and sorting them into the two categories, the team only had eight weighted criteria so they had the CS representatives add two more criteria to the list and then assigned a weight to each. *continued...*

Top 10 Weighted Criteria	Weight?
1. Pick up time/location is recorded electronically and accessible by CS.	9
2. Delivery data available online in real time.	10
3. Signature obtained upon delivery.	8
4. Possible to communicate with ground delivery personnel.	5

●●●

Part 2—Defining Desired Characteristics (DCs)

5. Ask the customer to brainstorm Desired Characteristics (DCs) of the final solution.

DEFINITION: A desired characteristic (DC) is any feature or function that the customer would like the final solution to have.

- Features are attributes of a product—"bells and whistles."

- Functions are what the product, service, process, or system will do, what function it will perform for the person using or interacting with it.

- DCs are wants—they are what the customer desires in a solution. They are not requirements. Requirements are a list of "must haves," and even though the team will be asking the customer to assign the DCs into categories later, which will include a "must have" category, this does not mean the customer will absolutely get the DCs that are in that category. This is because DCs are just that—desires. There is no commitment implied that customers will receive what they desire, but the team will use the DCs to construct a solution that is as close to the customer's desires as possible

- At the end of the *Solution Definition* process, the recommended solution, with its recommended features and functions, will be submitted for approval to the customer before the solution moves into development. If it is agreed upon, only then can there be a commitment on features and functions.

- Wants are different than needs. The need that the team explored with the *Needs Assessment* tool was the problem the customer was experiencing. Wants are what the customer would like to see in a solution.

- Write each DC in the left-hand column of a DC Table.

6. Ask for clarification on each DC so that it is clear what the customer is trying to communicate with each DC.

- Ask clarifying questions such as "how big?", "what duration of response time would be desirable?" etc.

- Each DC should clearly state what the customer wants, but preferably not in specific technical terms. Try to capture the DC "solution-free."

  - The technical solution to the DC is the prerogative of the innovation team, unless there is a good reason that the customer wants a specific technical solution.

- If a DC provided by the customer specifies a specific technical solution, then ask for a more general DC that describes what benefit the customer is looking for.

  - The technical experts will translate the DCs into technical requirements and apply whatever technology is most appropriate to getting the job done.

- If the customer is having trouble translating the DC into more general terms, then go to Step 7, and gather the information about why the DC is important to the business. That may help the team better understand the purpose of the DC.

> Do not argue with the customer. Do not try to convince them they are wrong. Instead, try to understand what need the DC meets for them. Remember, you're not committing to producing a solution that contains all of the customer's wishes, you're only collecting the customer's wish list.

TIP

7. Review the DCs for any missing characteristics. Eliminate any duplicates. Resolve any competing DCs.

- Have the customer review the table to identify any DCs that haven't been covered thus far.

- Review the table to see if there are any duplicates. If two DCs are very similar, combine them.

- Review the table for competing DCs—two characteristics that are mutually exclusive. Ask the customer to pick the one they prefer.

✐ 8. Ask the customer to explain why each DC is important to the business.

😊 Record the answer to the "why" question in the column labeled "Importance to Business" on the DC Table.

✐ 9. Have the customer rank each of the DCs.

😊 Add a column to the table for the ranking.

😊 Ask the customer to rank the DCs by one of the following:

> A = "must have"
>
> B = "highly desirable" and
>
> C = "nice to have"

😊 Remind the customer that not all DCs will be "must haves." If they are, then they've missed some DCs that belong in the other categories.

✐ 10. Have the customer rate the performance of the current system relative to each of the DCs.

😊 Use a 0-5 rating scale:

> 0 = nonexistent
> 1 = bare minimum
> 2 = slightly below average
> 3 = average
> 4 = above average
> 5 = world-class performance

NOTE: *Remember, these are the customer's ratings, their perceptions. If you don't understand the customer's reasons for the rating, ask for clarification, but don't argue with the customer!*

11. Have the customer set performance goals for the new solution.

- What level of performance is requested for each DC? Ask the customer to rate each goal using the 1–5 rating scale.

  - Remind the customer that ratings should be realistic. Not every DC can be a world-class performer, particularly if the current system is only performing at a level of 3 or less.

- Remember, this is not a commitment to meet the performance goals defined by the customer. You are just collecting data about what the customer wants. What can be delivered will depend on time, money, and people resources, as well as the availability of technology to create the performance levels desired. (The performance level that will be delivered will be communicated back to the customer in the *Solution Definition Document*.)

12. Calculate the net performance increase from the current system to the desired performance of the new system. Validate that the rating increases are consistent with the Type of Innovation.

- Subtract the rating for the current system (Step 10) from the performance goal rating (Step 11). This is the increase in performance being requested.

- Make sure the level of performance increase is consistent with the Type of Innovation (1, 2, or 3). If the innovation was intended to be a minor improvement and more than one or two of the DCs have an increase in rating of a A3 or 4, then the team should start to question whether this is, in fact, a minor improvement innovation. Major Improvement innovations (Type 2) will have some 3 or 4 ratings, and the team will need to use their judgment if the level of performance being requested can be accommodated by an improvement effort. If not, either the customer will need to scale back their expectations on performance increases or the team will need to think about shifting the effort to reinvention, which typically takes more time, effort, and money than an improvement project. With reinventions (Type 3), you expect more 3, 4, or 5 increases.

Part 3—Assess Competitive or Benchmarked Systems—Optional

✎ **13. Have the customer rate the performance of the competitor system or a benchmarked system relative to each of the DCs.**

☺ Is the customer familiar with any competing systems? Are there benchmarked systems to be considered? (A benchmarked system is one that is used by another organization and that is considered world class.) If so, have the customer evaluate each of these systems versus the DCs.

☺ Use a 0-5 rating scale as indicated in Step 10.

✎ **14. Compare the ratings for the current system with those of the competing or benchmarked system. Highlight the higher rating for each DC.**

✎ **15. Have the customer review, and if appropriate revise, the desired performance goals for the new system.**

☺ With the competitor or benchmarked data available, review the ratings set in Step 11. Revise as needed to ensure that the goals are adequate to meet future business needs.

- Also review to ensure performance goals are realistic relative to any benchmarked system.

- Recalculate the performance increase that has been requested.

The plan was to develop the solution internally, building onto an automated logistics system that existed in the firm's dispatch centers. A competitive system was being offered by a large systems integration firm that had extensive logistics experience working with the U.S. military. In order to decide between these two alternatives, the CS team evaluated both options. While the competitive system provided more infrastructure at the pick-up and delivery points, the automation in the centralized locations was not as up-to-date.

DC ⑤	⑨ Ranking	⑩ Performance Rating	⑪ Performance Goal	⑫ Amount of Increase	⑬ Competitor Rating	⑮ Final Performance Goal
1. Every delivery has a unique identifier	A	4	5	1	5	5
2. The system provides information in real time	A	0	4	4	2	3
3. Automated data entry of package pick-up & delivery	A	0	5	5	4	5
4. Record interim routing information	B	0	3	3	3	3

The team realized that although the competitive system outperformed what they had now, it did not meet their existing performance goals. They decided to develop their own system internally. The CS representatives, with the team, decided although they would really like to capture all signatures at delivery that maybe that was a DC that could wait until the next version and so they reduced its ranking and its performance goal.

Part 4—Resources Available

16. Have the customer define the resources available to complete the first stage of the solution.

- A solution can be rolled out in stages (see the *Vision Decomposition* tool) so not all of the performance goals need to be met in stage one of the solution

- Determine what the customer has available for resources for stage one of the solution:

  - How much time do they have? By when do they need a solution?

  - What is their spending limit?

  - How many people can they commit to the project and at what level of support?

The team determined that CS would like to have at least the first stage of the solution up and running in 18 months. With a spending limit of $250,000 they could devote two people, full-time and three people, at one quarter time. The team wasn't sure if these resource limits were realistic, but since they were not yet making a commitment to meet the DCs within the time frame and budget indicated, they chose not to worry about it.

7 IDEA GENERATION

Churn out lots of ideas

The Creativity Cycle starts with the gathering of data, usually through some type of research activity such as a literature search, searching the internet, interviewing people, observation, or experimentation. These are left-brained activities, meaning they are linear and logical. They are detail oriented and focus on the bits and pieces of information that are then stored in the brain's internal database.

The Cycle then moves into the *idea generation* phase, which is right-brained and holistic. The right brain thinks in patterns; it knits together the pieces of data that it accesses from the internal database in new ways. These are called ideas.

The Cycle then moves back to the left side of the brain where the validity of the ideas generated are tested to determine if they will hold up in reality.

The *Idea Generation* tool addresses the right-brained side of the Cycle: generating ideas. (The *Factorial Design of Experiments* tool can be used as a way to generate data for the left side of the Cycle.)

The Creativity Cycle

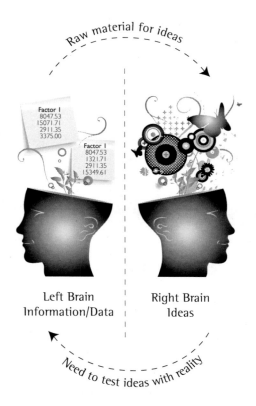

Raw material for ideas

Left Brain
Information/Data

Right Brain
Ideas

Need to test ideas with reality

Why do it?

- To generate new, unexpected ideas that can be synthesized into innovative solutions (see *Solution Synthesis* tool).

- To provide the basis for developing a breakthrough in thinking (see *Breakthrough Generation* tool).

- To allow the team to work with the data that they either collected or generated to see what insights might be derived from the data.

What does it do?

- Generates lots of ideas around any topic the team chooses that are then recorded and organized.

How do I do it?

Describe the topic that the ideas will address. The topic can be anything: how to create a desired characteristic, how to solve a specific problem, etc.

1. Collect the data available about the topic.

- Collect data and information to help fuel the idea-generation process.

  - Data can be collected by reviewing the literature, doing an internet search, reviewing patents, and trademark applications, etc.

- Data can be generated by experimentation.

---

2. Brainstorm and record ideas.

- Brainstorming is a process of allowing ideas to flow without judgment or analysis.

- Brainstorming can be done alone or with a group.

  - Brainstorm on your own

    - Keep an idea journal or a set of blank index cards with you at all times. Record ideas as they come to you: while reading, daydreaming, after jogging, or while doing any other repetitive activity. Write down every idea you have, no matter how ridiculous it may seem!

    - Sit down with some self-adhesive notes or index cards and just let the ideas flow. Follow the rules of brainstorming (see page 113 for Rules of Brainstorming)

  - Brainstorm with a group

    - Assemble a group to deliberately generate ideas related to a specific topic.

      - Include people who are familiar with the problem and with the data that was collected in Step 2.

      - Include outsiders—people who are unfamiliar with the problem and who are good at idea generation.

    - Remind everyone about the rules for brainstorming.

Rules of Brainstorming

1. No judging ideas while brainstorming.

2. All ideas are good ideas while brainstorming.

3. The more ideas the better.

4. The crazier the better. (Off-the-wall ideas give you a better chance of breaking out of the existing paradigm.)

5. No ownership of ideas. Piggy-back off of other people's ideas.

6. Record every idea. It's best to record the ideas on a self-adhesive note if you're working together in person.

7. Try to capture each idea as a complete thought, so it makes sense to everyone weeks from now!

8. Encourage the group to think outside the box. (See page 116 for tips on Helping the Team to Think Outside the Box)

TIP

After the group has picked the "low hanging fruit" of ideas and is losing steam, ask for just 10 or 20 more ideas. This will prompt the group to get more creative because they will have to stretch to reach for more creative ideas.

🙂 The team can list their ideas on a piece of flipchart paper, but the downside of this is that the ideas are stuck in the list and can't be easily moved in order to see relationships between them. A better method is to use self-adhesive notes. This will allow you to move the ideas around and organize them more easily.

CASE STUDY

The Bright Sunshine Coffee Company was looking for ways to expand the products and services they offered at their more than 100 coffee shops across the country.

Organize the ideas

🙂 If the team used self-adhesive notes, have the team sort the ideas into like groups. This can be done silently to avoid anyone dominating the sorting.

🙂 After the sorting is complete, have the group write headers for each of the groups.

Check with your patent attorney for recommendations on how to record ideas for patent purposes.

After the team finished brainstorming they silently sorted the ideas into groups and then discussed what the headings should be for each. This is a simplified version of the Affinity Diagram found in *The Memory Jogger™ II.*

Nonbusiness Services	Business Services	Business Products	Non-business Products
Private Parties	Copy Services	Office Supplies	Ice Cream/ Gellato
Speed Dating Services	Conference Rooms	Business Books	Smoothies
Evening Community Meeting Space	Office Space by Hour		Take-Out Lunches and Dinners
Wine Bar in the Evenings	Message Service		
Micro-brewery	Mailboxes and Shipping Services		
Book Signings			

Helping the Team
Think OUTSIDE the Box

1. Encourage the group to use analogies to prompt ideas. How is this problem like a bear (or other animal), a train (or other mode of transportation), a spoon (or other utensil), a chair (or other furniture)? By forcing the mind to make connections between very different concepts, you help it to break out of the box it's been in.

2. Ask the group to stretch the idea. How could we make this idea bigger? Smaller? Heavier? Lighter? More fluid?

3. Combine two dissimilar ideas and brainstorm ways to combine the two. What would it be like if we crossed idea A with idea B?

4. "What is the opposite of this idea?"

5. "Who else has this kind of problem, and what do they do to deal with it?"

6. Ask "What assumptions are inherent in our thinking? (Remember the problem of paradigms!) What would we do if our assumptions were not true?"

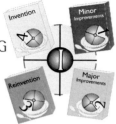

8 GENERATING BREAK-THROUGH IDEAS

Generate flashes of insight

Breakthroughs are big ideas that represent a major departure from how we thought about something in the past. They represent a paradigm shift from past ideas.

Breakthroughs are the outputs of the Breakthrough Cycle, which is, in turn, based on the Creativity Cycle, which you will recall from the *Idea Generation* tool. The Creativity cycle is a two-stage cycle that starts with the left-brained process of generating/collecting information and data, and then moves to the right-brained side where ideas are generated.

Breakthrough ideas appear as flashes of insight after you've worked the Creativity Cycle over and over and over again. At some indeterminate point, when it seems like you'll never get that breakthrough idea, the insight flashes into your mind, and you've got it!

The unpredictability of the breakthrough idea makes it particularly exciting when the flash finally happens. But the flip side of that coin is that that unpredictability also makes it impossible to know when the breakthrough will occur; thus planning becomes problematic. So, when a breakthrough idea is needed in an innovation project, make sure you include plenty of contingency time (reserve time) to cover the uncertainty that will always exist around the generation of breakthrough ideas.

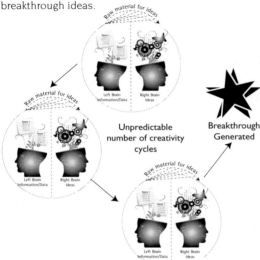

The Breakthrough Cycle

To enhance your chances of creating a breakthrough, try the following:

✍ 1. Immerse yourself in the problem you're trying to solve.

(☺) When you're going for a breakthrough, it's best not to work on multiple innovation projects. You need all your brain power to be devoted to that task of generating the breakthrough.

- The brain is like a computer—the more programs you have running, the slower the performance.

2. Collect lots and lots of data. Generate lots and lots of ideas.

- The more data and ideas you pour into your brain, the more material it has to work with.

- You may have to generate lots of ideas that are not viable to get a few really great ones. And it usually takes cycling through lots of not very good ideas to finally create the platform for generating the final breakthrough idea.

- Generate wild and crazy ideas. The crazier the ideas, the more likely you are to break out of the box/paradigm your current thinking is stuck in.

3. Explore the paradigm of the system you're trying to generate the breakthrough for. Use the Paradigm Deconstruction and Paradigm Construction tools.

- The paradigm tools provide richer sources of raw material to work with in exploring a breakthrough.

- Be aware of paradigm concepts from other fields that might be useful for the breakthrough you're trying to achieve.

4. Explore concepts from other fields.

- When you explore concepts from other fields, you open your mind up to data that you wouldn't have encountered otherwise. It can also help in creating a paradigm shift.

- Have people from other fields review the data and ideas you've collected thus far. They may be able to help you make connections that haven't occurred to you because you're too close to the situation.

5. Practice a repetitive activity that disengages the left brain.

- Breakthroughs happen when the left brain is disengaged giving the right brain a chance of getting its ideas through. To disengage the left brain, do something "boring," that doesn't require a lot of focused attention, such as running, taking a shower, or meditating.

6. Keep a dream journal and write it down.

- Breakthroughs are sometimes communicated in dreams. Examples of discoveries that were made as a result of dreams include:
  - Kekule discovered the structure of the benzene ring.
  - Mendeleyev dreamed up the organization of the elements into the periodic table.
  - Banting dreamed of a new approach to isolating insulin.
  - Howe received the insight on how to create a lock-stitch sewing machine.

7. Use symbols to tap into the right brain.

- Bring in a deck of tarot cards. (That isn't a misprint!) The tarot images are symbolic and thus are great tools to help the right brain create new associations between the symbol and the topic you're trying to generate a breakthrough about. They are particularly useful if you're trying to create a breakthrough involving a service, because the cards represent various archetypal (common to all of humanity) situations that humans find themselves in and thus are particularly apropos to service situations.

- Use any deck, spread the cards face down on a table. Have someone in the group pick a card and then have the group brainstorm ideas on how a solution could be like the card that was picked.

It's better not to know what the cards are *supposed* to mean so you can brainstorm straight from the images.

8. Keep an idea notebook.

- As the Creativity Cycle gets rolling, you'll find you have ideas popping up at all times of the day or night. It's important to capture those ideas, no matter how far-fetched they may seem. Keep an idea notebook with you at all times. Every time an idea pops into your mind, WRITE it DOWN! Enter the date you had the idea.

9 PARADIGM CONSTRUCTION

Building ideas for new mental models

New paradigms are the basis for creating breakthroughs in technology and for finding new concepts for solutions. But creating a new mental model is tricky business, because we are so immersed in the existing paradigm that we have trouble seeing anything outside of it. (See Chapter 4 for more information on paradigms.) Paradigms are like the air that we breathe. We take them completely for granted. They are givens in our lives. That is why deconstructing the existing paradigm is so important (*Paradigm Deconstruction* tool). After you have identified the components or elements of the current paradigm—the boundaries, concepts, rules, and assumptions—as well as identifying the problems that paradigm has not been able to resolve, then you have the raw materials you need to begin constructing a new one.

Why do it?

If the team is working on an invention or reinvention effort, then shifting paradigms is key to getting to the breakthroughs necessary to build a truly innovative, new solution. The best way to shift a paradigm is to take apart the elements of the old paradigm and then combine them in different configurations to generate potential new paradigms.

The Process of Building New Paradigm Ideas

Elements of Deconstructed Paradigm	Brainstorm New Elements	Ideas for New Paradigms
Boundaries	Ideas for ways to change the boundaries	
Concepts	Brainstorm new concepts	
Rules	How can the rules be bent? Changed? Reversed?	
Assumptions	What exists that might challenge assumptions of the paradigm?	
Unsolved Problems	How would the paradigm need to change in order to solve the unsolved problems?	

What does it do?

- Challenges the elements of the old paradigm, its boundaries, concepts, rules, and assumptions, and then uses those raw materials to brainstorm ideas for a new one.

- Generates multiple options for a new paradigm of technology or a new concept for a solution.

How do I do it?

1. Start by challenging the assumptions of the old paradigm. If the evidence for an assumption does not hold up to scrutiny or is not valid outside the rules of the paradigm, brainstorm new assumptions that could take its place. Collect evidence for the new assumptions.

- Challenge the assumptions of the old paradigm by doing one or more of the following:

  - Ask the question, "Is the assumption universally true or just true within the context of the existing paradigm?"

    - If it's true only within the context of the paradigm, then it's a belief, not a fact.

  - Conduct research—review the literature, review patents if appropriate, look at related fields for new information that could challenge the assumption.

  - Conduct experiments—if the assumption lends itself to experimental testing, then test whether or not the assumption is true. (Tools such as the *Factorial Design of Experiments* tool can be helpful for testing)

  - Observe—consciously look for anomalies to the assumption:

- An anomaly is anything that doesn't fit into the existing paradigm.

- Since we view the world through our paradigms, you have to make a very deliberate choice to begin noticing things outside your mental model. For example, if you believe it's true that people cannot be trusted (an assumption), then you would need to look for situations in which this assumption is not true to test, in order to test whether or not your assumption is universally correct.

  - When you find instances in which the assumption isn't true, write them down. This will help you stay focused on what you are looking for and provide evidence that your assumption is not correct.

- Once you find an assumption that doesn't hold up to testing, observation, or rational thought, then brainstorm alternative assumptions.

- For each new assumption, determine if there is evidence to support it.

The ABC Airline innovation team deconstructed the existing paradigm for the airline passenger service business, (refer to the *Paradigm Deconstruction* tool for more information on the analysis of the existing paradigm), and they felt they understood the concepts, rules, and assumptions that drove the airline industry to that point.

The team decided to challenge the assumption that the hub-and-spoke system was the best way to manage the routing of flights. This model routes all flights from secondary markets into an airline hub (within a primary market) and then back out to a secondary market. The team determined that the hub-and-spoke assumption was a belief and therefore was open to challenge.

The team brainstormed some new assumptions:

- ❑ The shortest distance between two points is a straight line. **Fact.**
- ❑ Direct flights are preferred by most travelers. **Fact. There is evidence to support it.**
- ❑ What is now considered a segment could be considered a flight. **Belief.**
- ❑ Loads can be maximized on individual flights. **Belief.**
- ❑ Most people are flying from and going to secondary markets. **Fact. There is evidence to support it.**
- ❑ It is of benefit to dominate a market. **Belief.**
- ❑ Operating costs are less when you dominate the gates at an airport. **Fact. There is evidence to support it.**

●●●

2. Based on the new assumptions, create new rules and concepts that could be the basis of a new paradigm.

- 😊 Brainstorm ways in which the new assumptions would change the rules and concepts of the existing paradigm.

- 😊 Build new rules and concepts based on the new assumptions.

> "Talk through" or use thought experiments (emulate Einstein!) to explore the possibilities of the new paradigm.

CASE STUDY

The team created some new rules for their new paradigm:

- ❏ A flight is a nonstop trip between any two cities.

- ❏ The passenger must figure out how to combine flights to get from one destination to another.

- ❏ Dominate secondary markets not primary ones.

- ❏ Since routes are shorter, no meals will be served on any flights.

- ❏ The airline will compete on price. *continued...*

The new concepts might be:

❏ Loads are maximized within individual flights.

❏ Passengers book the flights they need to get them from their departure city to their destination city. Each segment is a separate flight and is managed by the airline as an individual unit.

❏ The airline offers a no-frills approach to flying—no snacks, limited beverage service— in order to keep costs low.

❏ The airline will use both the low-cost flights and the no-frills approach as competitive and marketing advantages.

3. Using the unsolved problems of the old paradigm, create ideas for how to change the rules, assumptions, and concepts for a new one.

What's not possible with the old paradigm? What assumption or rule changes would need to be made in order to make what's impossible, possible?

What assumptions or rules would you need to change in order to solve one or more of the unsolved problems of the old paradigm?

The unsolved problem the team tackled first was "It is hard to sell middle seats, particularly on long flights." The rules and concepts that applied were:

❑ Seats must be assigned either at ticketing or at flight check-in.

❑ Aisle and window seats are preferred over middle seats.

The team explored how the existing rules make it difficult to sell middle seats. Passengers choose their seat assignments when booking the flight and some prefer to opt for a different route or a different airline if aisle or window seats are not available. So the team wondered what would happen if they changed those rules? They came up with some ideas for new rules:

1. Passengers will be assigned a seat at check-in, based on first-come, first-seat choice.

2. No seats will be assigned. Passengers will just get on the plane and decide where they want to sit.

3. Aisle and window seats can be purchased ahead of time, but they will cost more.

The team decided to explore the possibilities for new rule #2. They combined this idea with the one they had for eliminating classes of services (no first-class or business-class seats). Eliminating the classes of service would permit more seats

continued...

to be put on a plane, free up the front restroom for use by everyone on the plane, and simplify the food service by eliminating meals and alcohol for first-class service (which would no longer exist). It would also expedite boarding as there would be no frequent flyers awaiting the possibility for last-minute class upgrades. The team thought that if seats were not assigned at all the problem of people switching airlines to get an aisle or window seat could be eliminated. It would also expedite the boarding process.

4. Explore what it might mean if the boundaries of the current paradigm were changed.

🙂 Brainstorm ways in which you could move the boundaries of the existing paradigm. What might be possible that's now not possible?

5. Continue to play with challenging assumptions, rules, concepts, and boundaries, and then test any new paradigm ideas that seem promising.

🙂 Create as many new ways to change the old paradigm as possible. Let yourself get "wild and crazy." This helps the breakthrough process.

🙂 After you've brainstormed some possible changes to the paradigm, find ways to test whether these ideas might work. You can test by:

　🙂 running experiments (*Factorial Design of Experiments* tool) on assumptions.

　🙂 creating a model or simulation of the new paradigm in order to test it.

- Researching facts that might support your new hypothesis.
- Trying to challenge the assumptions of your new paradigm. Do they hold up to scrutiny?

The team examined the assumption that assigned seating did indeed delay boarding and sometimes flight departures by examining FCC-reported causes of delayed departures across all airlines for a 90-day period. They found that of the total delayed flights, 8 percent were due to duplicated seats and another 9 percent were due to other reseating issues. While they were unable to tease out this last statistic they knew from their own data that approximately 3 percent of all flights annually reported problems with class upgrades creating tension between the customer and the gate/flight staff.

The team also examined the fundamental assumption that only business travelers were profitable. They developed a financial model by which in-flight service was stripped down to the basics and boarding procedures expedited with a simple first-come, first-in process with no assigned seats. Less food service would mean cleaner planes and faster turnarounds, allowing 2.75 more flights per day. Pricing models were simplified so that there were basically two types of fares: supersavers that incurred additional fees for itinerary changes and full fares that did not. Smaller planes were also budgeted, resulting in fuel and capital cost savings. The final result showed that, even with increased advertising to promote this service among non-business travelers, the new service would indeed be highly profitable.

10

SOLUTION SYNTHESIS

Combining ideas into solutions

The *Solution Synthesis* tool is used for building solutions. A solution is a complex mixture of features, functions, and technology. Solutions are built from "raw materials" or elements that were generated with other tools, such as data and ideas generated about a problem, its causes (if appropriate), criteria, and desired characteristics, ideas, breakthroughs. as well as elements created with this tool: options for features or functions of the solution and options for technologies that could be used to solve the problem. All of these raw materials are mixed up, combined in different ways, hybridized, pulled apart, and then put back together again. This is a synthesis process, the combining of two or more elements to create a whole new one, that is greater than each of the separate parts.

The result is a set of ideas for solutions aimed at resolving the gap that triggered the whole innovation process in the first place.

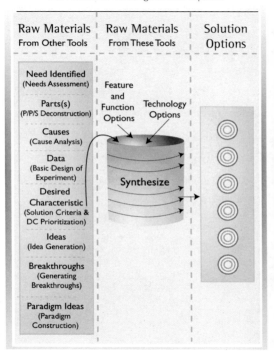

Raw Materials From Other Tools	Raw Materials From These Tools	Solution Options
Need Identified (Needs Assessment)	Feature and Function Options	
Parts(s) (P/P/S Deconstruction)	Technology Options	
Causes (Cause Analysis)		
Data (Basic Design of Experiment)	**Synthesize**	
Desired Characteristic (Solution Criteria & DC Prioritization)		
Ideas (Idea Generation)		
Breakthroughs (Generating Breakthroughs)		
Paradigm Ideas (Paradigm Construction)		

Why do it?

- Solution synthesis is one of the key tools in the creation process because it produces a variety of options that will then be filtered, assessed, and decomposed in preparation for final *solution selection* (the Solution Selection tool).

It forces the team to think beyond the obvious solutions, to think outside the box and come up with a variety of options that then can be considered further.

What does it do?

Takes the data and ideas the team has generated thus far and adds to it ideas for features, functions, and technology to create a variety of options for solutions to the customer's problem.

How do I do it?

1. Review the rules of brainstorming.

The *Solution Synthesis* tool is basically a brainstorming tool that utilizes many pieces of information. Therefore, it's important to keep in mind all the rules of brainstorming (see page 113), particularly the rule about NO judging of ideas.

2. Gather all the data that the team has collected or generated thus far and review it with the team.

See page 134 for the types of data that might be utilized for the synthesis of solutions.

- You don't need all the data shown on page 134 to generate a solution for your innovation. Use the *Innovation Type Guide to Tools* on page xi as a guideline for which tools will provide the types of data the team needs based on the Type of Innovation it is working on.

Review the data collected so that all the team members are familiar with all the raw materials that will be used in this tool.

3. Review the technologies that were used to build the current system. Brainstorm technology options.

- Review the technologies used in the current system.
  - Technologies are a set of tools or techniques used to get something done.
  - Technologies are used to build parts of a system or to hold the parts together. Make sure everyone on the team understands what technologies were used in the current system.

- Brainstorm alternative technologies that could be used to improve or replace the current system.

- Refer to the information generated with the *Needs Assessment* tool to see what desired characteristics (DCs) and performance goals were requested. Brainstorm technologies that would enable the team to build those DCs and attain those goals.

CASE STUDY

The Longevity Corporation, a large hospital system, chartered a team to come up with the best possible solution to the problem they were experiencing: not being able to successfully execute their strategic plan. Their strategic plan laid out the goals that would lead them in the direction in which they desired to go. To reach those goals, innovations would be needed, but the organization, thus far, hadn't been able to achieve the innovations that would be needed to execute the plan.

The team worked through the gap analysis and was then ready to synthesize solutions. At first,
continued...

---

they were a little confused about how technology might apply to their situation, but once they started brainstorming, they came up with technologies that could contribute to a solution:

❏ *Innovation technology*—Methodology associated with the innovation process.

❏ *Creativity technology*—Methods for generating creative ideas.

❏ *Project management methodology*—Method to coordinate the activities of a project. At Longevity, each project manager currently chose his own method and so there was no common technology for managing projects. Most of these methods were directive in approach.

❏ *Intervention technology*—The team had explored the way in which the Project Support Office (PSO) interacted with projects in trouble and found they had also used a directive technology when intervening with teams.

❏ The PSO used Microsoft Project® to track the progress of projects.

❏ There was no system in place to select, fund, and prioritize projects across the organization. Each function tended to start its own projects and then struggled to get people from other functions to participate in them.

❏ The leadership team uses an MBO technology to decompose the goals of the strategic plan and deploy them through the functional organization. *continued...*

The team brainstormed for technology options:

Innovation technology—Train project leaders and teams in the innovation tools found in this Memory Jogger.

Creativity technology—Train project leaders and teams in the creativity tools found in *The Creativity Tools Memory Jogger™*.

Project management methodology—Roll out a standard project management methodology that is cross-functionally focused and that is built on a participative rather than a directive model.

❑ One team member suggested they could use the method found in the *Project Management Memory Jogger™*.

Technical processes—Standardize and streamline each technical process, such as software development and new product development.

Intervention technology—Use a collaborative intervention technology for teams in trouble.

❑ Utilize web-based technology to provide the PSO with "early warning" bells that a project is in trouble so interventions can occur before a project is in crisis.

Portfolio technology—Bring in a cross-functional portfolio management process for selecting, funding, and monitoring the portfolio of projects at a business-leader level.

●●●

4. Brainstorm possible features and functions to include in a solution.

Using the raw materials available, brainstorm ideas for new features or functions of potential solutions.

TIP

Refer back to the *Needs Assessment* for the Desired Characteristics (DCs) provided by the customer. Include those in the list of features and functions. Add to the list any features and functions the team thinks would help achieve the performance goals.

CASE STUDY

The innovation team realized that the innovation system they would be designing would have to start with strategy creation and deployment, and then resource allocation, execution, and project monitoring. They would also need to examine the abilities of individuals and teams to work through the innovation process. A new innovation system would require support, particularly while the organization was learning how to use the new system and its tools. The team felt that project management was a subset of innovation, since any significantly sized innovation was also a project. In fact, they thought the innovation system and the project system would need to be integrated.

The team realized the solution they were creating was going to be so large they would need to divide it into segments that they could brainstorm separately: Strategy development,
continued...

Project/Portfolio System, Innovation Support, Innovation Methodology, Individual Innovation, etc. The team decided to tackle each segment separately, synthesizing solutions for each. Although it didn't really matter which segment they brainstormed first, the team decided to start by generating ideas for Innovation Support:

❏ Convert the PSO into the Center for Innovation Excellence (CIE). Have the CIE support all innovation projects, or set up a new Center for Innovation Excellence (CIE). Have the PSO report to the CIE.

❏ Have the CIE train all leaders, including project leaders, in the innovation process.

❏ Standardize the key technical processes and train employees so they don't have to reinvent them when used in a project (such as developing a new piece of software).

❏ Use the CIE to support a cross-functional leadership council that would oversee the portfolio of innovation projects.

❏ Have the PSO or CIE focus on prevention by working with teams during the Gap Analysis and Solution Selection Stages so innovation projects are headed in the right direction.

❏ Create an early warning system so the PSO/CIE knows when a project is heading for trouble so it can intervene earlier.

❏ Have a collaborative audit process that periodically reviews all projects.

●●●

✐ 5. Brainstorm solution options.

◉ Look at different combinations of features, functions, and technologies that could be used in building a solution.

　◦ Brainstorm features and functions that could be included in solutions that would solve the customer's problem.

> As with any brainstorming activity the wilder the ideas, the better. Don't hold back! Get creative and go for extreme ideas for solutions. Analyze later—those that won't work will be eliminated, so there is nothing to lose in thinking outside the box.

> If the team is large (more than 5), break up into subgroups of three to four. Each subgroup should come up with as many solutions possible using the raw materials provided. After brainstorming, bring the groups back together and review the solutions generated. Find ways to synthesize more solution options based on the ideas generated by each subgroup.

◉ Try to come up with at least a half dozen options for solutions.

　◦ The first two options will probably come quite easily. The next few will be more difficult and will require the team to generate more creative ideas.

The innovation team took the ideas for features, functions, and technologies and brainstormed four different solution options for Innovation Support:

1. Convert the PSO to a CIE. The CIE would focus on building capability by training leaders and teams in innovation and project management skills. It would provide support to the Portfolio Management segment of the solution.

2. A new CIE would be created and the PSO would report to the CIE. The CIE would oversee the whole innovation system. It would support Portfolio Management. The group that oversees business process improvement would also report to the CIE.

3. A new senior leader position would be created —Chief Innovation Strategy Officer (CISO)— and the staff needed to support the innovation system would report into the CISO. The CISO would head up a cross-functional Innovation Steering Council that would manage the portfolio of innovation projects. It would also set standards for innovation and project management methodologies.

4. The PSO would be converted to a CIE and would focus on consulting during the first two innovation stages: *Gap Analysis* and *Solution Definition*, with the intent of starting the project off right and thus eliminating the need for interventions later. It would support a cross-functional Innovation Steering Council that would manage the portfolio of innovation projects. ●●●

11 SOLUTION FILTER

Narrow down the solutions

After the team has generated ideas for solutions (using the *Solution Synthesis* tool), it's time to narrow down the choices so that the team can ultimately come to consensus on the best possible solution for development (*Solution Selection* tool).

The *Solution Filter* tool uses Go/No Go decision criteria for filtering a large number of solutions down to the few that best meet the customer, stakeholder, and sponsor criteria for a successful solution. (The best way to generate those decision criteria is using the *Solution Criteria & DC Prioritization* tool.) After the number of potential solutions has been reduced to two to four choices, each filtered solution is analyzed for strengths and weaknesses. Then the team comes up with ideas for overcoming the weaknesses and records them as countermeasures.

Why do it?

☺ To quickly eliminate solutions that do not meet Go/No Go criteria, so that the team can concentrate on gathering more data on the select few solutions that have the highest potential to creatively solve the customer's problems.

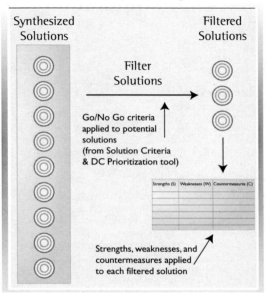

Synthesized Solutions

Filtered Solutions

Filter Solutions

Go/No Go criteria applied to potential solutions (from Solution Criteria & DC Prioritization tool)

Strengths (S)	Weaknesses (W)	Countermeasures (C)

Strengths, weaknesses, and countermeasures applied to each filtered solution

☺ By defining the strengths and weaknesses of each potential solution it provides data that will be used in assessing each of the filtered solutions using the *Technical Difficulty*, *Solution Impact Risk Assessment*, and *Adoption Assessment* tools.

What does it do?

☺ Uses Go/No Go criteria to narrow down the number of solution options.

- Analyzes the strengths and weaknesses, and ways to overcome the weaknesses (called countermeasures) of the filtered solutions.

How do I do it?

⟋ 1. Gather a combined list of Go/No Go criteria from the customer, stakeholders, and sponsor.

- If the team used the *Solution Criteria & DC Prioritization* tool then it has already collected Go/No Go criteria from the customer. This tool can be used to collect criteria from stakeholders as well!

- The sponsor's criteria represent the needs of the organization relative to a solution.

  - Organizational criteria are usually associated with costs, deadlines, technology to be used, etc.

  - Example: Cannot cost over $100,000.

- Go/No Go criteria are used to eliminate solutions that do not meet basic qualification criteria.

  Go/No Go criteria can also be used as an initial screening option when you have numerous possible solutions.

  - Criteria only fit into the Go/No Go category if a "No" answer kills the solution as an option.

⟋ 2. Refine the combined list of Go/No Go criteria to ensure no viable solutions would be eliminated as a result of the criteria. Validate the final list with the customer and sponsor.

- Go/No Go criteria are black and white: if the solution does not meet just one of the criteria, the solution is a "No Go" and it is eliminated from further consideration. Therefore, be careful in picking No Go criteria.

- The criteria should be stated so that a "yes" answer includes a solution as an option to be evaluated against the next criterion, and a "no" answer eliminates a solution altogether.

- Check to see if there are any conflicting criteria. If there are, resolve the conflict by eliminating one of the criteria or by rewriting both to eliminate it.

- Once satisfied with the list, have it reviewed and signed off by the customer and sponsor.
  - If the customer is external to the organization, then have the customer representative(s) validate the criteria on behalf of the customer.

CASE STUDY

It's 1980 and the XYZ Company assembled an innovation team to automate the routing of its expedited delivery of package services. The Client Service (CS) group is the customer for the project and the team pulled together their criteria for a solution shown below. (For more information on the case, see the *Solution Criteria* and *Desired Characteristics Prioritization* tool.) The team gathered criteria from other stakeholders including:

❏ The innovation sponsor, whose criterion was that the project had to be completed within an 18-month time period.

❏ The Ground Delivery group, whose representatives had a No Go criterion of no additional time required for pickup and delivery. *continued...*

❑ The Information Technology team, which supports the dispatch centers and also had a criterion to ensure that the data captured by the new system could be integrated with the scanning technology currently in use.

The combined list of all criteria is shown below, along with their Go/No Go status.

Criteria ①	GO/NO GO? ②
1. Pickup time/location is recorded and accessible by CS.	
2. Must know the status of the location of a package during the delivery process.	YES
3. Delivery data available in real time.	
4. Signature obtained upon delivery.	
5. Possible to communicate with ground delivery personnel.	
6. Metrics on overall delivery performance on a periodic basis by route, driver, dispatch, and receipt center.	
7. Completed within 12 months.	YES
8. Integrates with the scanning technology currently in use at dispatch and receipt centers.	YES
9. Aggregated volume statics on a daily basis.	
10. Scans of actual delivery signatures available to CS online.	
11. Completed within 18 months.	YES
12. No additional time for pickup or delivery of packages.	

3. Run the potential solutions through the finalized Go/No Go filter.

For each solution option (generated with the *Solution Synthesis* tool), analyze the solution versus each Go/No Go criterion. Document which criteria it passes (a "GO") and which it fails (a "NO GO").

The team had generated four possible solutions:

Solution A: Carbonless copy forms in quadruplicate (one receipt per pickup location, delivery location, dispatch, and receipt centers) would be used and scanned into the tracking system at receipt and dispatch centers.

Solution B: Photos taken at pickup and delivery locations are then scanned into the tracking system at receipt and dispatch centers.

Solution C: Time-elapse technology embedded in document packaging indicating, with color changes, elapsed time in transit.

Solution D: Portable punch-clock technology used at pickup and delivery.

Criteria ①	Solutions A	B	C	D
1. Status location of package during delivery process.	Go	Go	No Go	No Go
2. Automated alert notification to CS if a problem occurs that would delay deliveries (such as planes grounded for bad weather).	Go	Go	Go	Go
3. Completed within 12 months	Go	Go	Go	Go
4. Integrates with the scanning technology currently in use at dispatch and receipt centers.	Go	Go	No Go	No Go

4. Remaining solutions, use an S/W/C Analysis.

S = **Strengths** = how it solves the problem; how easy it will be to adopt.

W = **Weaknesses** = how it doesn't solve the problem, or how it will be difficult to adopt.

C = **Countermeasures** = How the weaknesses can be overcome.

For each solution, brainstorm all the strengths in one column and weaknesses in the next. Then, list countermeasures or actions that could be taken to overcome the weaknesses of the solution.

The team eliminated Solutions C and D and was left with the carbonless forms solution (Solution A) and the photo solution (Solution B). They did an S/W/C Analysis on each. Carbonless form solution results:

Strengths (S)	Weaknesses (W)	Counter-measures (C)
Easy to implement with delivery personnel	More paper that must be stored or destroyed	Implement special scanning procedures with dedicated staff to minimize lag time between delivery activity and data entry into tracking system
Available now	Can be torn, lost, or ruined	
	Time lag for entry of data into the tracking system	Implement immediate destruction procedures once form is scanned
Provides record of delivery	More personnel required for data entry	Create clear plastic sleeves to protect forms attached to documents in transit

12

VISION DECOMPOSITION

Stage solutions to reach a vision

The *Vision Decomposition* tool takes a potential (or selected) solution and projects it into the future to create a long-term solution or vision that will meet the future needs of the customer. (Part 1 of the tool.) However, it's usually not possible to create the long-term solution with one innovation effort, because it's either too technically difficult or it's too much for the customer and stakeholders to adopt. Therefore, it's helpful to break that vision down into a series of short-term, staged solutions, each of which: a) is manageable (the team can successfully organize and execute it), b) is technically feasible, and c) will be adopted by the customer and stakeholders. This is called "staged innovation," which is also called "multi-generational planning," with each stage a "generation" (Part 2 of the tool). This is also called "multi-generational planning."

Why do it?

To explore what the ultimate or long-term solution would look like. This sets a direction for interim innovations and provides the customer with a vision of the solution they will have when all the innovations are created and adopted.

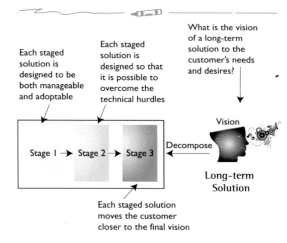

Each staged solution is designed to be both manageable and adoptable

Each staged solution is designed so that it is possible to overcome the technical hurdles

What is the vision of a long-term solution to the customer's needs and desires?

Vision

Stage 1 → Stage 2 → Stage 3 ← Decompose

Long-term Solution

Each staged solution moves the customer closer to the final vision

The Result of Vision Decomposition

- To make sure that the solution the team develops can be successfully implemented.

- Provides data that can be used for selecting the solution (*Solution Selection* tool).

What does it do?

- Defines a vision of what the ultimate solution to the customer's problems would look like to ensure each innovation project is headed in the right direction—toward the ultimate, long-term solution.

- Breaks down a long-term solution into a series of short-term ones, each of which is feasible, manageable, and adoptable.

How do I do it?

Part I—Create the Long-term Vision of the Solution

🖎 1. Describe the ultimate solution that will meet the customer's long-term needs.

😊 Describe a solution that would meet the needs of the customer three, five, or even ten years into the future.

- 😊 What's long-term for one solution can be short-term for another. Work with a time dimension that is long-term for the business that the customer is in.

😊 What features and functions would the long-term solution have?

- 😊 Identify broad features of the solution. This is not meant to be done at the micro level.

- 😊 Refer to the Needs Assessment data for the wish list defined by the customer.

CASE STUDY

The senior leaders of the research and development organization within the Peters Pharmaceutical Company decided that it was time to look at a new way to structure and manage their organization. They chartered an innovation team to come up with a solution to the problems they had been experiencing including:

❑ There was little or no cooperation between functional departments.

continued...

❑ There was no accountability and a lot of blame and finger-pointing. when things went wrong

❑ Leaders don't know how to manage without authority.

The team spent time in diagnosing the problem and felt it boiled down to two key factors:

1. Most of the organization work involves multiple functions but they are not set up to be managed cross-functionally.

2. Leadership and accountability are based on the need to have authority to get things done, but most of the work occurs in cross-functional teams over which the very senior people have no direct authority.

The team investigated possible solutions to the problem and arrived at a vision that would employ the new matrix management technology for managing the organization cross-functionally, without relying on authority. (This new matrix management is different than the unsuccessful technology used in the 1980s.)

✐ **2. Identify the major technical challenges or hurdles that will have to be overcome in order to get to the vision. Identify the major adoption hurdles.**

☺ Technical challenges can include actual technical difficulties involved in building the long-term solution, as well as obstacles related to changing current practices and systems.

Use the Technical Difficulty Assessment tool to identify all the technical hurdles associated with any staged innovation project.

🙂 What individual or organizational capabilities must be developed, learned, or imported?

🙂 What are the greatest challenges to getting the long-term solution adopted by the customer and stakeholders?

Use the Adoption Assessment tool to identify all the adoption issues related to any staged innovation project.

CASE STUDY

The team was primarily concerned about adoption of the new matrix. They knew that their vision involving people learning to think and act differently would threaten people's sense of power. They determined the adoption hurdles to be:

❏ People not understanding where the new matrix solution was headed.

❏ Leaders reluctant to give up authority and control to achieve accountability.

❏ The belief that it's faster to tell people what to do than to work through a collaborative process.

❏ Lack of skills in collaborative management approaches.

❏ The time to learn new ideas and skills. ●●●

Part 2—Decompose the Vision into Staged Innovations

✍ 3. Break the final vision down into staged innovations.

☺ Break the vision down into a series of technically achievable, adoptable solutions.

 It's best to keep each staged solution as simple as possible, thus reducing complexity and technical difficulty.

☺ Guidelines to structuring the series of staged projects include:

- ☺ Keep each staged project as small as possible, but big enough that customers and stakeholders can recognize a real difference.
- ☺ Keep each staged project as short as possible.
- ☺ Don't try to overcome too many technical difficulties or adoption issues in one stage.

 If the stage is too ambitious, the team can easily flounder and not accomplish anything. It's better to create a smaller, less ambitious project to begin with, complete it successfully, and then tackle the next doable project.

✐ 4. Define the outputs of each of the staged projects. Identify in very rough terms (+/- 50%) the resources needed for each staged project.

☺ What will be produced by each staged innovation project?

   ☺ Describe the output of the first stage in detail.

☺ Describe the resources needed to achieve the first stage.

   ☺ How many people will be needed to work on each stage? (This is a rough estimate, so provide a range, i.e., from 20 to 35 people.) Are there any unique skills required?

   ☺ How long will each stage take? (This is also a rough estimate so provide a range, i.e., from 6 to 12 months.)

   ☺ How much will it cost? (Estimate to within +/- 50 percent)

CASE STUDY

The innovation team worked hard on breaking their vision down into staged solutions. They came up with the first three stages and decided they would reassess their decomposition of the vision after the completion of each stage.

continued...

Stages	Description	Output
1. Project System Stage	– Collect projects into a portfolio managed by a cross-functional leadership team (project steering council). – Implement a collaborative project management methodology across the whole organization. Ensure good planning and execution of projects will introduce more collaboration. – Train sponsors to direct/ oversee innovation projects.	– A portfolio of projects managed/aligned with the strategic plan – A standard, collaborative project management method used on all projects – Trained project sponsors
2. Accountability Stage	– Introduce the new system so leaders understand their organizations accountability, such as defining their team and individual accountabilities. – Train employees to create accountability contracts. – Train employees in collaborative decision-making and problem-solving methods.	– Defined accountability for all strategic goals, subgoals, and deliverables – Accountability tools in use – Teams that can make decisions quickly and effectively
3. Relationship Management Stage	– Train managers to act as coaches to their employees. – Train managers to manage internal customer/supplier relationships. – Train leaders in team and individual communication skills.	– Matched with a trained coach – Internal customer/supplier relationship defined and functioning more effectively

13

TECHNICAL DIFFICULTY ASSESSMENT

Assessing how to overcome technical hurdles

Part 1 of the *Technical Difficulty Assessment* tool helps a team to identify the obstacles or technical hurdles standing in the way of developing the solution. After each deliverable and the corresponding technical hurdle are identified and rated, countermeasures, or ways to overcome the difficulties, are developed. The output produced by the team is called the Technical Difficulty Table.

Output of the Technical Difficulty Assessment

Types of Innovation ①		Rating ④	Counter- measures ⑥
Interim ② Deliverable	Technical ③ Hurdles		
1.			
2.			
3.			
4.			
Overall Level of Technical Difficulty ⑤			

Part 2 of the tool, which is used during the Development Stage of the innovation process, helps the team to: a) monitor their progress in overcoming the technical hurdles identified during the *Solution Definition Stage*, and b) continually reassess the technical difficulties that remain in the project.

Why do it?

- To identify how to overcome technical obstacles for either: a) one of several possible solutions, or b) the solution chosen for development.

- To communicate to the customer, stakeholder, and sponsor what technical hurdles the team will face in creating a successful solution so that expectations about the difficulty of the project are in line with reality.

What does it do?

- Lays out the team's plan for overcoming the technical hurdles associated with a solution and defines the resources needed to make that happen. (Part 1)

- Rates the overall difficulty of developing the solution being considered. (Part 2)

- Provides a way of tracking how the team is progressing in resolving the technical difficulties identified. (Part 2)

How do I do it?

Part 1—Assessment—Usually done during the Solution Definition Stage

⚗ **1. Indicate the "Type of Innovation" represented by the potential solution.**

🖐 Types of Innovation (from Chapter 1).

> Type 1 = Minor improvement
>
> Type 2 = Major improvement
>
> Type 3 = Reinvention
>
> Type 4 = Invention

⚗ **2. Identify the interim deliverables that the
team will need to develop in order to create the
identified solution.**

DEFINITION: An interim deliverable is an output
that is created in the process of developing the
solution for the customer.

🖐 Break the potential solution down into interim
deliverables.

  ◦ An interim deliverable is a "thing"—either tangible or intangible—that is produced as a result
of a series of tasks or steps in a process

  ◦ The process might be the writing of a report.
The interim deliverable is the first draft of the
report. Or, the process might be building a
table. The interim deliverable is the legs.

⚗ **3. Brainstorm the technology hurdles that will
need to be overcome in order to create each of the
interim deliverables.**

🖐 Many, if not most, of the interim deliverables will
not have any technical hurdles, so it's not necessary to create ones where they don't exist!

🖐 Technical hurdles don't need to involve a "technology" problem. They are simply obstacles that

---

must be overcome in order to create the interim deliverables. An example of a technical hurdle for creating this tool might be "coming up with a case example that is not too complex and that is distinct from the examples used for other tools."

4. For each interim deliverable, rate the overall level of difficulty in producing that deliverable.

On a scale of 0 to 5, rate the magnitude of the technical difficulty involved in developing the interim deliverable.

> 0 = "no brainer"—no difficulty in creating the deliverable
> 1 = very minor difficulty
> 2 = minor difficulty
> 3 = moderate difficulty
> 4 = high level of difficulty
> 5 = very high level of difficulty

5. Rate the overall level of difficulty for developing the solution.

Review the ratings for the interim deliverables and then rate the overall difficulty for the entire solution on the 0-5 scale (as described in Step 4).

The higher the difficulty rating, the more contingency time and money are needed to support developing that solution. However, there are no set guidelines on how much contingency to add for each overall rating since the rating scale is subjective. Any team that has a solution which falls into the 4 or 5 rating category should consider decomposing the solution into staged solutions. (See *Vision Decomposition* tool.)

6. For each interim deliverable rating of a 3 or higher, generate ideas for how to overcome the technical hurdles.

- Gather a group of technology experts to generate ideas (see *Idea Generation* tool) about how to overcome the technical hurdles associated with each deliverable rated a 3 or higher.

- The ideas for overcoming obstacles or technical hurdles are called "countermeasures."

7. Create criteria for selecting countermeasures. Select the countermeasures that meet the defined criteria.

- Determine the criteria the team will use to select the best possible countermeasures to overcome the technical hurdles. Criteria to choose from might include:

  - Will effectively overcome the technical hurdle.

  - Is a cost-effective approach to overcoming the technical hurdle.

  - Can be done within the timeframe of the innovation project.

  - The expertise to deploy the countermeasure is available to the team.

- Select those countermeasures that meet the defined criteria and include them in the Technical Difficulty Table.

Sunshine Petrolia is an oil refinery that produces gasoline and other fuel products from crude oil. There refining process, feedstocks are fed into the process and the output is one of several possible refined fuels (such as gasoline or diesel fuel).

Ratings of crude oil supplies and other feedstocks, their costs, and the market data for fuel products are all tracked manually. To efficiently utilize its refinery resources, to better match feedstock supplies and refining capacity with market demand, and to properly track costs, Sunshine's innovation team determined it should automate these manual systems and integrate them with the automated refinery operations management system.

After identifying interim deliverables, technical hurdles, and possible countermeasures, the team compiled a list of criteria to help them choose which countermeasures to include in their plan:

❑ Countermeasures effectively overcome hurdles

❑ Don't create more manual steps to the system

❑ Are consistent with researched best practices for similar systems in the chemical industry

Part 2—Updates and Tracking—Usually done during the Solution Development Stage for the selected solution.

✐ **8. Periodically review the assessment done in Part I and update as needed. Revise the ratings for remaining interim deliverables. Review overall** rating for the solution. Revise the overall technical difficulty rating for the solution.

Technical Difficulty Table

Types of Innovation ❶	3			
Interim Deliverable ❷	Technical Hurdles ❸	Rating ❹	Countermeasures ❺	❻
1. Online data collector of suppliers' feedstock information	• Accepting the different data formats from each crude oil supplier • Guaranteeing that the importation of data from suppliers does not alter data integrity • Maintaining the unique identity of every lot of feedstock through the ratings and matching system	4		
2. Feedstock ratings engine	• Automating the heretofore manual rating calculation using cost and grade data • Creating exception overrides for the ratings engine that can be applied to a specific feedstock supply • Updating feedstock pricing databases in real time as the market changes	5		••••
Overall Level of Technical Difficulty ❼		3		

- As the team creates upstream interim deliverables, more information on technical difficulty will be available about downstream deliverables. Therefore, it's useful to update the Technical Difficulty Assessment periodically, which means:

  - At important stage gates (decision points in the process at which a major chunk of work has been done and the project is up for a Go/No Go review) or

  - At regular intervals, such as quarterly if the project is of longer duration, (a year or more) or more frequently if it's a shorter project

- To update the assessment, repeat Steps 2 through 7 again.

  - It's not necessary to start over from scratch. Simply review the work done previously and see if any of it needs to be updated.

  - Rerate the technical difficulty for interim deliverables not yet completed.

9. Periodically publish the updated Technical Difficulty Table.

- The Technical Difficulty Table is an important communication tool that keeps everyone up to date on how the work is progressing. If the ratings change, include the revised table in the team's status report.

14

SOLUTION IMPACT RISK ASSESSMENT

Reduce the risk associated with a solution

Part 1 of the *Solution Impact Risk Assessment* (SIRA) tool is used to determine what could go wrong (the risks) after a solution is launched. The team brainstorms all the potential problems, or risks, that could occur and creates a grid diagram that shows: a) the degree of negative impact that each risk would have if it did occur and b) the probability or likelihood of each risk occurring. The team then brainstorms risk responses or countermeasures to reduce or eliminate the risk. The team also rates the overall risk associated with the solution before and after countermeasures are applied.

The *Solution Impact Risk Assessment* differs from a Project Risk Assessment in the following ways;

Solution Impact Risk Assessment: Evaluates the risks related to what the solution might do to the groups/environment it interfaces with after launch. It also defines risks that might occur after the project is completed.

The Project Risk Assessment: Evaluates the risks of not meeting scope, schedule, or budget targets during the project. It also defines risks that might occur during the project.

Part 2 of the tool is used by the team during the Development Stage to continually reassess the risks that the solution might pose to its environment and to come up with new ways to prevent those risks.

The Grid Diagram for the Solution
Impact Risk Assessment tool

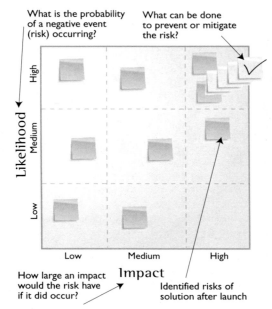

What is the probability of a negative event (risk) occurring?

What can be done to prevent or mitigate the risk?

Likelihood

High

Medium

Low

Low   Medium   High

Impact

How large an impact would the risk have if it did occur?

Identified risks of solution after launch

Why do it?

☺ Provides information about the potential down-sides that a solution might have on its environment after it is launched. This information can be used to compare potential solutions before selecting the best possible solution (*Solution Selection* tool).

What does it do?

☺ The *Solution Impact Risk Assessment* identifies and rates all the risks associated with the solution after launch. It rates the overall risk level of the solution—before and after countermeasures are applied; allowing you to create a plan for how to overcome the risks identified. It also provides a way of tracking risks and countermeasures during development. (Part 2)

How do I do it?

Part I—Assessment—Usually done during the Solution Definition Stage

1. Identify the best team to participate in the Solution Impact Risk Assessment.

☺ Include project team members.

☺ Invite technical experts who are familiar with the technology that will be used to build the solution.

☺ Make sure to include customer representatives in the group to identify downstream consequences.

(☺) Include experts in environmental hazards if the solution interfaces with the physical environment.

✍️ 2. Have the team identify any known problems that the solution will create after its introduction. ⸰

(☺) If there are problems that are certainties, things that will definitely happen, then identify those first.

(☺) Place each known problem on a self-adhesive note (the 3"X3" size works best) and place it on a piece of flipchart paper labeled "Known Problems."

✍️ 3. Brainstorm all the risks (potential problems) that might occur after the solution is introduced. Describe why each one is a risk.

(☺) First, establish the rules of brainstorming, see page 113.

(☺) Identify the interface groups/systems that the solution will be in contact with.

Note: *The Context Diagram tool will help the team to identify the interfaces.*

(☺) Brainstorm the potential problems (risks) that the solution could create for each of the interface groups/systems. Write each risk in the center of a self-adhesive note.

Bad Loans

Compensation Risk for AE's & CC's

Venture Capital Fund Exposure

Personal Guarantees Needed

Loss of Private Bank Business

✐ **4. Analyze what the magnitude of the impact would be if the risk did occur. For medium and high ratings, describe the impact and quantify if possible.**

👤 If the risk did occur, how significant an impact would it have?

👤 Use a Zero, Low, Medium, and High scale to rate the impact ("I").

Name of risk
I

> ☺ A Zero rating means it will have no impact and the potential problem can be discarded
>
> ☺ Low impact = minimal cost, liability, negative impact on brand, minor impact on customer satisfaction, etc.
>
> ☺ Medium impact = moderate cost, liability, impact on brand and customer satisfaction, etc.
>
> ☺ High impact = large cost, liability, etc.

Consider having the team make a short list of examples for low/medium/high for more uniform scoring among team members.

👤 Describe the cost of any risks with a medium or high impact rating.

> ☺ How much money would it cost?
>
> ☺ How much effort and time would be required to deal with it?
>
> ☺ What would the legal liability be? What would the impact of a lawsuit be on the company and brand image?

- Would there be an impact on the relationship to the customer? To the team where it is a stakeholder? What would it be?

- What other costs are associated with the risk?

5. Analyze the likelihood that each of the negative impacts might occur.

- Rate the likelihood ("L") that each potential negative impact (risk) will occur.

  - Use a Zero, Low, Medium, High, and Certain scale.

Zero =	There is no likelihood of the event occurring; therefore, the risk can be discarded
Low =	low likelihood that the risk will occur
Medium =	medium likelihood the risk will occur
High =	high likelihood that the risk will occur
Certain =	If it's certain that the negative impact will occur, then it's not a risk, it's a known problem. Move it to the Known Problems sheet.

  ```
  Name
  of risk

  L        I
  ```

  - Another option is to use a 0-10 scale instead. A 10 would be a known problem, so those would be moved to the Known Problems sheet. A 0 would be no probability, so those would be discarded. Ratings of 1-3 would be a small likelihood, 4-6 would be a medium likelihood, and 7-9 would be a high likelihood.

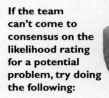

If the team can't come to consensus on the likelihood rating for a potential problem, try doing the following:

❑ If the the team doesn't consider the risk to be very important, then use the average of each team member's ratings.

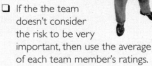

  ❑ Value a low rating as a "1," a medium rating as a "3," and a high rating as a "5" to calculate the average.

❑ If the risk is important, then take the upper value and ask the group to list all the reasons why the risk should be rated in this way. Then do the same for the lower value. Then do one of the following:

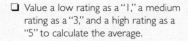

  ❑ Challenge the assumptions to see which one holds up best and/or collect data to determine which is most likely to be correct.

TIP

6. Create a 3X3 grid diagram with Likelihood on the left-hand side (y-axis) and Impact on the bottom (x-axis) and place the self-adhesive notes on the grid.

😊 Line up the lower left-hand rating from the self-adhesive note with Likelihood on the y-axis.

😊 Line up the lower-right hand rating from the self-adhesive note with Impact on the x-axis.

7. Assess the overall Risk Rating for each risk.

😊 The overall Risk Rating for each risk is based on where on the grid it appears. Risks that are in the lower left-hand two boxes are low risks. High risks are in the upper right-hand boxes and mediums are in the middle. Write the overall Risk Rating in the bottom center portion of the Note.

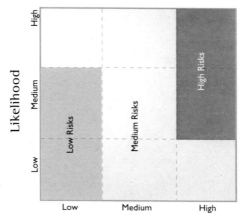

Bilbo Bank, a small national commercial bank ($10 billion in assets), had carved out a very profitable niche by focusing on lending to high-tech start-up companies that had been funded originally by venture capitalists. The bank was now seeing increased competition from unregulated financial companies (especially leasing and insurance firms), which did not have the same regulatory requirements for documentation and credit worthiness of debtors.

The bank assembled an innovation team to come up with a solution to the problem of unregulated lenders. The team came up with an innovation called the Supersonic Loan, which was an expedited loan process directed at its current target market. The team included representatives from the line of Account Executives (AEs), the Credit Coordinators (CCs) who assist AEs with loan origination and documentation, and the Credit Committee to whom AEs and CCs present loans for bank approval. The AEs were the representatives of the customer, the high-tech start-up company. They also represented the key stakeholder—the venture capital (VC) funds that were funding the start-up.

After identifying the risks, and rating them for impact and liklihood, the team placed their notes on the grid and calculated the risk rating for each individual risk.

continued...

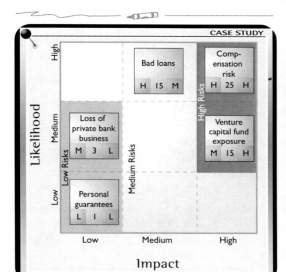

8. Based on the grid diagram, assess the overall risk for the solution.

If there are any risks in the high-risk category, then the solution is a high risk. If there are no high risks, but there are medium-level risks, then the solution is a medium risk. If there are no high or medium risks, then the solution is a low-risk solution.

9. Rate the team's overall confidence in the Solution Impact Risk Assessment.

How much confidence does the team have that they've captured all the risks?

Rate the team's overall confidence on a 1 to 5 scale.

> 1 = very low confidence
> 2 = low confidence
> 3 = moderate confidence
> 4 = high confidence
> 5 = very high confidence

10. Record the team's work in the Solution Impact Risk Assessment Table.

Set up a table with the following columns; Risks, Likelihood Rating, Impact Rating, Description of Impact, Overall Rating.

11. Brainstorm countermeasures to prevent or reduce each risk that has a risk rating of medium or high, and for each known problem.

Come up with all the ways in which a risk could be prevented or reduced.

12. Select the countermeasures to include in the risk response plan and then assign accountability for each countermeasure.

Pick the countermeasures that have high effectiveness (will provide the greatest reduction in risk) and low cost (time and money).

After the team has selected the countermeasures, assign someone to be accountable to ensure each one gets done.

(☺) Record the countermeasures that will be included as part of the solution plan on the Solution Impact Risk Assessment Table.

✎ **13. Rerate the likelihood and impact ratings for each risk. Reassess the risk rating for each risk taking into account the countermeasures that will be implemented.**

(☺) Taking the countermeasure into account, rerate the likelihood and impact of each risk. Cross off the old risk rating in red on the self-adhesive note and write the new rating above it. Move the risk to the new spot on the grid and record the risk rating associated with that block on the grid.

(☺) Update the Solution Impact Risk Assessment table

✎ **14. Reassess the overall risk of the solution when countermeasures are included.**

(☺) If there are any risks still in the high-risk category after countermeasures are accounted for, then the solution is still a high risk. If there are no high risks, but there are medium-level risks, then the solution is still a medium risk. If there are no high or medium risks, then the solution is a low-risk solution.

(☺) Update the Solution Impact Risk Assessment table.

Solution Impact Risk Assessment Table

Risk ①	Chosen Countermeasures ⑫	New Likelihood Rating ⑬	New Impact Rating ⑬	New Overall Rating ⑭
1. Compensation risk	Modify compensation plan regarding Supersonic program loans, provided that AEs and CCs comply with 100% of the program's requirements & procedures.	L	L	L
2. Venture Capital fund exposure	VCs will require their portfolio managers to fully cooperate with the Supersonic process and all its requirements, thus limiting both the banks, exposure and their own.	L	L	L
3. Bad Loans	The VC's backing the applicant companies will be required to guarantee the loans for up to 75% of total loan value.	M	M	M
4. Loss of Private Bank business	- N/A	M	L	L
5. Personal guarantees from start-up management	- N/A	L	L	L
	Solution Impact Rating 14			M

The team managed to reduce the Supersonic program from high risk to medium risk with the addition of countermeasures.

Part 2—Updates and Tracking— Usually done during the Solution Development Stage for the selected solution

✐ **15. Periodically review the assessment completed in Part 1 and update as necessary.**

- As the team works on developing the solution, more information will be generated about the solution and its potential impact on its environment after it's introduced. Therefore, it's useful to update the *Solution Impact Risk Assessment* periodically:
  - Just before important stage gates (decision points along the process where a major chunk of work has been done and the project is up for Go/No Go review), or
  - At regular intervals, such as quarterly if the project is of longer duration (a year or more), or more frequently if it's a shorter project.

- To update the assessment, review the work done previously and see if any of the assumptions have changed. If they have, rerate the risk, add a new risk, remove a risk, etc.

✐ **16. Periodically publish the updated Solution Impact Risk Assessment table.**

- The Solution Impact Risk Assessment table is an important communication vehicle for keeping everyone informed about how the project is progressing. Include it as part of the status report on the project.

15

ADOPTION ASSESSMENT

Overcoming resistance factors

An *Adoption Assessment* is done when the team wants to identify what types and levels of resistance might be encountered in getting the customer (and stakeholders) to adopt a solution.

The team first identifies and rates all the changes that will be made when switching from the old solution to the new. They then identify all the problems that will be solved by the new solution.

Adoption Assessment Table

Old Characteristics ❶	New Characteristics ❶	Level of Change ❷	Type of Change Required ❸	Problem Solved ❹
1.				
2.				
3.				
4.				

Part of the Adoption Assessment Table

Next, the team brainstorms everything that could get in the way of the customer (and stakeholders) adopting the solution. Each possible reason that the customer might not adopt (called a resistance factor) is analyzed for its probability or likelihood of occurring and its importance or impact on the adoption process. A grid diagram is created that shows the level of resistance inherent in the solution (based on how the resistance squares are distributed on the diagram). The team then brainstorms ways to overcome those resistance factors with countermeasures, the best of which are included in the plan for developing the solution.

In Part Two of the tool, the team monitors adoption resistance to see if the factors they identified in Part One are decreasing, staying the same, increasing, or if new ones are popping up. This allows the team to continually revise its strategy about how to move the solution toward full adoption at launch.

Why do it?

- To Identify the benefits of the new solution, which forms the basis for the messaging used in the *Communication Plan* tool.

- To uncover anything that could get in the way of adoption and create a plan for addressing it before launching the solution.

- To select a solution that is both doable *and* adoptable.

What does it do?

- Identifies the changes that the new solution will bring to the customer and stakeholders.

The Grid Diagram & Resistance Scale for
the Adoption Assessment Tool

What is the probability of the resistance factor occuring?

What can be done to prevent or mitigate the risk factor?

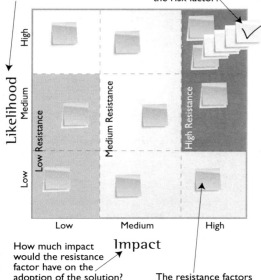

Likelihood

High

Medium

Low

Low Resistance

Medium Resistance

High Resistance

Low   Medium   High

Impact

How much impact would the resistance factor have on the adoption of the solution?

The resistance factors

Adoption Resistance Scale

Before countermeasures

1   2   3   4   5

After countermeasures

(ಠ) Identifies and then rates all foreseeable adoption resistance factors.

(ಠ) Generates ways (countermeasures) to address each significant resistance factor. The team then chooses the best countermeasures to include as part of the adoption plan.

(ಠ) Tracks the progress of overcoming resistance to the adoption of the selected solution. (Part 2)

How do I do it?

Part 1—Assessment—Usually done during the Solution Definition Stage

✏ **1. From the point of view of the customer, list the characteristics of the old system that will change and the new characteristics that will take their places.**

> You'll need to have customer representatives in the group to help the project team identify the customer-based changes.

Note: *When assessing resistance for stakeholders, just replace the word "Customer" with the word "Stakeholder" in the steps below.*

(ಠ) In the column labeled "Old Characteristics" in the Adoption Assessment table, record the characteristic that the customer has now that will change (improvement, replacement, deletion).

(ಠ) In the second column, list the new characteristics that the customer will have to adopt.

- When adding new characteristics where old ones did not previously exist, just write "none" in the "Old Characteristics" column and then describe the new characteristic.

- If a characteristic is being dropped, write "none" in the "New Characteristics" column.

Note: *Some characteristics involve very small changes and therefore can be combined into a larger characteristic, assuming they fit together from the customer's point of view.*

✍ 2. Rate the level of change the customer will need to make in order to adopt each characteristic listed in the table.

- On a scale of 0 to 5, rate the magnitude of each change from their customer's emotional/behavior point of view.

0 = no change
1 = very small change
2 = small change
3 = moderate change
4 = difficult change
5 = very difficult change

- Complete the third column, "Level of Change" in the Adoption Assessment table.

Adoption Assessment Table

Old Characteristics	New Characteristics	Level of Change	Type of Change Required
Weekly sales rep reports	Sales reps will report daily online	5	Daily reporting online will be a major change since most reps dedicate several hours on Friday afternoons to doing manual reports. In the future they will spend half an hour at the end of each day to complete the report online.
Manual system	Automated online system	4	Reps and leads will need to be trained to enter data and management will need to be trained to retrieve information.
Lack of standards in reporting	Standardized definitions embedded in new system	4	Sales, proposal preparation, and contracting will have to learn and conform to the new standards.
Reentry of data required by accounting	New system will integrate with commission and accounting systems, eliminating reentry of data	2	Accounting clerks will have less to do.

✐ 3. Describe the change the customer will have to make in order to adopt the new feature.

☺ Describe any and all changes, even ones that appear to be positive.

  ☞ NOTE: *We don't always embrace positive change! If we did, everyone would eat only healthy food. Therefore, think about all the changes that would need to be made, even the positive ones.*

  ☞ Changes are actions that must be taken. Changes could include things such as purchases they will have to make, actions they will have to take that are different than the actions they take now, changes in staffing or training, or abandoning an action taken before.

☺ Fill in the fourth column, "Type of Change Required" in the Adoption Assessment table.

CASE STUDY

A clinical laboratory organization (CLO Unlimited) that supports clinical trials for pharmaceutical companies pulled together an innovation team to address their problems with manually produced weekly sales reports that are then rolled up by sales managers into a monthly sales report for the leadership team. In addition, proposal/bidding reports are completed each week by the Proposal Preparation Group and are not integrated with the sales report even though proposals are part of the sales process. No reporting has been required from the Contract group, which is also part of the sales process.

continued...

The solution being assessed by the innovation team is an online system that sales reps would update remotely, at the end of each day, and that proposal leads and contract leads would update whenever any activity on a proposal or a contract has been completed. The reporting from the system would be visible to each rep, proposal lead, contract lead, and the entire leadership team. The new system would provide the leadership team with real-time access to information, starting with a lead for a new account and ending with the contract signing for a specific clinical trial.

✐ **4. To highlight benefits for the stakeholders, list the problems that will be solved as a result of the proposed changes.**

👁 The problems the potential solution will solve may or may not cover all the problems identified in the Needs Assessment. Or there might be as-yet-unidentified problems that the proposed solution will resolve. List all problems that would be solved as a result of the potential solution.

✐ **5. Brainstorm possible resistance factors that might block the customer from adopting the proposed solution and write each resistance factor on a self-adhesive note.**

👁 A resistance factor is any condition that would impede the customer from taking the actions that are needed in order to make the changes identified in Step 3.

😐 Resistance factors can usually be traced to psychological or emotional changes someone will have to make in order to adopt the change.

😐 Put yourself in the customer's shoes as you think about how you would feel if you had to make the changes identified in Step 3. When thinking about resistance factors, consider the following questions:

  ⌣ How attached is the customer to the current solution? Will their security, power base, or self-esteem change as a result of the change?

  ⌣ What might they lose that is of value to them?

  ⌣ What kind of resistance might arise from having to do things differently than they do them now?

  ⌣ What do they have to let go of? What might get in the way of letting it go?

Remember that even things that are considered positive change are nonetheless changes and involve a degree of letting go, disruption, uncertainty, fear, risk.

😐 Resistance factors also have to do with changes in day-to-day routines. What kind of disruptions will the changes create in the customer's ability to fulfill their daily tasks?

  ⌣ How much disruption will be involved in day-to-day life when making the change? The larger the disruption, the more resistant people are to adopting a new solution.

  ⌣ How might it negatively affect the daily workload during transition?

  ⌣ What type of additional training or new skills might be required?

6. For each adoption factor, rate the likelihood of resistance being present and the impact the resistance would have, if real, on the adoption of the solution.

- Rate the likelihood of the resistance factor as being a real factor in the customer's adoption of solutions.

  - Use a zero (0), low (L), medium (M), or high (H) rating scale

    > **0 Likelihood** = no resistance exists and the note can be discarded
    >
    > **L Likelihood** = the resistance factor has only a slight chance of occurring
    >
    > **M Likelihood** = the resistance factor has a 50-50 chance of occurring
    >
    > **H Likelihood** = the resistance factor is likely to occur

  - Write the likelihood rating (L, M, or H) on the bottom left-hand corner of the self-adhesive note.

- Rate the Impact of the resistance.

  - The Impact factor means that if the resistance did occur, what level of impact would that resistance have on the adoption of the solution?

  - Again use a rating scale:

    > **L Impact** = minor effect on the adoption of the solution
    >
    > **M Impact** = moderate effect on the adoption
    >
    > **H Impact** = significant effect on the adoption

  - Write the impact rating (L, M, or H) on the bottom right-hand corner of the self-adhesive note.

✐ 7. Create a 3X3 grid diagram of resistance factors and place the resistance factor self-adhesive notes in the appropriate box on the diagram.

☺ Draw a 3X3 grid diagram with Likelihood along the y-axis (left side) and Impact along the x-axis (bottom).

☺ Add the resistance factor adhesive notes to the grid, matching the lower left-hand corner Likelihood rating with the y-axis, and lower right-hand Impact rating with the x-axis.

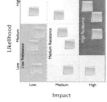

☺ A grid diagram is shown above. The overall level of resistance is shown by the shades of the boxes. For example, the two lower left boxes represent low resistance factors.

✐ 8. Assess the overall adoption resistance for the solution as a whole.

☺ Review the grid. Based on the distribution of the notes on the grid, rate the overall resistance of the customer to adopting the solution. (For example, if the notes are equally distributed, then there is a medium or moderate resistance to adoption.) Use a 1 to 5 scale to rate the overall resistance:

1 = very small resistance	**Adoption Resistance Scale**
2 = small resistance	Before countermeasures ▼
3 = medium resistance	
4 = large resistance	┤ 1 ┤ 2 ┤ 3 ┤ 4 ┤ 5 ┤
5 = very large resistance	

9. Brainstorm ways to overcome each resistance factor. Select the best ideas to use as countermeasures. Rerate the likelihood and impact for each resistance factor after the selected countermeasure(s) is applied.

- Brainstorm ideas for ways to prevent or overcome any resistance factors that fall into the medium-and high-resistance areas on the grid diagram.

  - Write each idea for a countermeasure on a self-adhesive note.

- After the team has finished brainstorming, select the most effective countermeasures that require the least amount of time and money, and place a check mark next to them to indicate the countermeasure will be included as part of the overall adoption plan.

- Rerate the likelihood and impact ratings for each resistance factor taking into account the application of the selected countermeasure(s).

> Usually it is the likelihood rating changed by countermeasures since it's easier to reduce the probability of something happening than it is to reduce its impact.

TIP

Countermeasures that involve communications should be included in the Communication Plan that is developed with the Communication Plan tool, page 211.

The team brainstormed countermeasures for factors in the medium and high categories on their grid diagram. Here is a sample of a completed form for one of the resistance factors.

Adoption Assessment Table

Resistance Factors	Likelihood/ Impact Rating	Countermeasures	Check Countermeasures Chosen	New L/I Ratings
Sales reps have new daily reporting routine	H/M	Demonstrate the time savings of daily reporting versus weekly reporting	✓	L/M
		Select an "evangelist" from within the ranks of the sales force to promote the new system		
		Sales managers will allocate half-an-hour of sales rep's time each day so they can enter the required data	✓	
		Ask sales reps to participate in the design of the system	✓	

✍ 10. Assuming the countermeasures selected will be implemented, reassess the overall adoption resistance for the solution as a whole.

Part 2—Updates and Tracking— Usually done during the Solution Development & Implementation Stages for the selected solution

✍ 11. Periodically review the assessment done in Part 1 and update as necessary. Publish the updated results.

- As the team works through the Development and then Implementation stages, more information will be generated on adoption resistance; therefore, it's useful to update the adoption resistance table periodically:

  - Just before important stage gates (decision points along the process where a major chunk of work has been done and the project is up for Go/No Go review), or

  - At regular intervals, such as quarterly if the project is of longer duration (a year or more), or more frequently if it's a shorter project

  - To update the assessment:

    - Review each resistance factor and the countermeasures implemented to date.

    - Revise the ratings to reflect current status.

    - Brainstorm more countermeasures if needed.

    - Brainstorm any new resistance factors and create countermeasures.

    - Update the overall resistance rating (after countermeasures).

16

SOLUTION SELECTION

Choose the Best Possible Solution

The *Solution Selection* tool analyzes the solutions that passed through the *Solution Filter* against a set of Weighted Criteria to select the "best possible solution." The best possible solution is not necessarily the most elegant or technically advanced solution. Instead, it's the one that best fits the set of criteria developed with the customer, sponsor, and stakeholders. (See the *Solution Criteria & Desired Characteristics* (DC) *Prioritization* tool.)

Why do it?

☺ Using a structured process helps the team come to consensus around the best possible solution.

☺ To document and communicate the rationale for selecting that solution for development.

What does it do?

☺ Assesses the degree of fit between each solution and each weighted criterion.

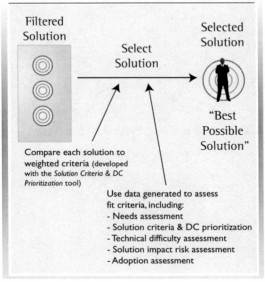

Compare each solution to
weighted criteria (developed
with the *Solution Criteria & DC
Prioritization* tool)

Use data generated to assess
fit criteria, including:
- Needs assessment
- Solution criteria & DC prioritization
- Technical difficulty assessment
- Solution impact risk assessment
- Adoption assessment

Generates data that indicates which solution
best fits the criteria for selection.

Describes the features and functions of the
selected solution.

How do I do it?

 1. **Establish a set of criteria for selecting the
best possible solution for the customer, key stakeholders, and the sponsor. Establish weights for each
criterion.**

- Create a set of criteria for evaluating each potential solution:

  - The criteria were defined by the customer, stakeholders, and sponsor using the *Solution Criteria & DC Prioritization* tool. The weights assigned with that tool were based on the importance of the criteria to the customer. In the *Solution Selection* tool, the criteria from all sources—customer, sponsor, stakeholders—must be aggregated and a new, combined weight must be assigned.

  - Add any criteria that the team feels is important based on assessment results: Technology Assessment, Adoption Assessment, and the Solution Impact Risk Assessment.

- A weight is a measure of how important a criterion is relative to whatever solution is selected. Use a 1-to-10 scale for assigning weights.

> 1 = the criterion is extremely unimportant.
>
> 5 = the criterion is moderately important.
>
> 10 = the criterion is extremely important.
>
> Based on the scale above, a weight of 8 would mean a very important criterion. A weight of 3 would mean a very unimportant criterion.

TIP

Some criteria will be more important than others, so try not to give all the criteria the same weight, which only defeats the purpose for assigning weights in the first place.

Solution Selection Matrix

Criteria	Weight	Solution Option 1	Solution Option 2	Solution Option 3
A	10			
B	8			
C	7			
D	6			
E	5			
F	3			

2. Set up the solution selection matrix for performing the analysis.

- List the criteria for selection in the first column.

- Write the weights in the second column.

- Write the name of each solution option in each of the remaining columns.

- Now the team synthesizes several potential solutions to the problem of an Innovation Portfolio Management System (IPMS). They came up with the following options:

1. **Project Support Office Steering**—The Project Support Office (PSO) would manage the portfolio of innovation projects—selecting those projects to be included in the portfolio, allocating resources to selected projects, and then monitoring the projects as they moved through the pipeline.

2. **Innovation Steering Council (ISC)**—A senior level, cross-functional steering team would be created that would collectively select, prioritize, fund, and monitor the portfolio of innovation projects. The PSO would provide the ISC with the data it would need on the status of projects. Resource managers would provide resource information.

3. **New Innovation Function**—A new Innovation Strategy function would be created that would manage the innovation project portfolio.

4. **Strategic Planning Group**—The current strategic planning function would be converted to a strategic planning/innovation portfolio management function.

The team had collected criteria using the *Solution Criteria & DC Prioritization* tool and so they were able to set up the Solution Selection Matrix very easily.

3. Compare each solution against each criterion and rate the degree of fit. Place the rating in the upper left-hand corner of the cell where the solution and the criterion intersect.

For example, compare Solution 1 against Criterion A and rate as follows:

0 = no fit; does not satisfy criterion
1 = very minor fit; minimally satisfies the criterion
3 = moderate fit; half satisfies the criterion
5 = excellent fit; fully satisfies the criterion

If there is disagreement on the degree of fit, determine the basis for the difference in opinion. Are there different assumptions? Do people have different perceptions? Different data?

TIP

- If the criterion has a low weight (1) and therefore isn't critical to the overall decision, see if the group would be able to accept an average of everyone's rating.

- If the criterion has a medium to high weight (3 or 5), then have someone advocate for the higher rating and someone advocate for the lower. See if the group can reach consensus. If not, then determine what the team would need, in the form of more information or data, to come to consensus on the degree of fit.

- If the team needs to do additional testing to determine how well the solution will fit the criterion, determine how best to gather the data.

See Factorial Design of Experiments tool as one method for generating data

If the team used the *Solution Filter* tool to identify strengths, weaknesses, and countermeasures, evaluate the degree of fit for each solution assuming the countermeasures are included.

TIP

- If the Degree of Fit Rating for Solution 1, Criterion 1 was a 3 and the weight for the criterion was an 8, then the weighted rating to place in the bottom right hand corner of the cell is 24.

Weighted Rating

3

24

Degree of Fit Rating

- Add up all the weighted ratings (the ones in the bottom right-hand corner of each cell) for a single solution. Record the total.

✏️ **5. Choose the best solution.**

- Based on the Solution Selection matrix results, come to consensus on which solution has the best fit for the customer, the stakeholders, and the organization.

  - Consensus:

    - A decision based on consensus does not mean that everyone necessarily agrees that it is their first-choice decision. It does mean that everyone agrees to support the decision.

    - Once a decision is made, everyone has the responsibility to support it with their constituencies and stakeholders.

Don't just let the numbers rule. Check the group's intuition about the decision. Does the solution with the highest total make the best sense? If not, explore why not. Review the criteria and their weights. Are they correct? Review the team's assumptions about each solution. Are they correct? Are the ratings for fit right? If the team can't find anything wrong with the logic, then the solution with the highest overall rating is the best possible solution.

If the team used the *Solution Filter* tool to identify strengths, weaknesses, and countermeasures and evaluated the degree of fit for each solution with the countermeasures included in Step 3, then go back and rerate the solutions without the countermeasures included. Then, based on the cost of applying the countermeasures for each solution, determine which solution makes the most sense.

TIP

CASE STUDY

The innovation team for Longevity, a large hospital system, created a vision for an Innovation System that the organization could use to ensure its strategic plan was executed creatively. They broke down the vision into stages, with the first stage addressing the Project System. As part of that system, the team needed to decide what kind of Innovation Portfolio Management System (IPMS) the organization should use. The IPMS

continued...

would be the process by which the leadership team would select, fund, and monitor all of its innovation projects.

The team reviewed the results from the Solution Selection matrix and the best possible solution ISC composed of leaders from across the business. Before accepting that as the solution, they discussed why it met the criteria and made the most sense. First of all, no additional resources would be required since the cross-functional leaders already exist. They would be able to make the high-level priority decisions based on the needs of the business better than the other proposed steering groups. They also had more access to resources than a support group would have. Having existing leaders in charge of the portfolio of innovation projects would help to instill a culture of innovation in the organization.

The team determined the degree of fit and the weighted rating for each cell in the matrix. They then totaled each column to determine which solution had the highest overall rating.

6. Define the actual characteristics to be included in the selected solution. Explain any differences between the actual characteristics to be included and those requested by the customer.

Translate the desired characteristics (from the *Solution Criteria & DC Prioritization* tool) into the actual characteristics to be included in the solution.

- 😊 Work with any resource constraints imposed by the customer and sponsor.

- 😊 Keep the language in nontechnical terms so the customer can understand what will be delivered.

	Solutions – Steering				
Criteria	Weight	PSO	ISC	New Innovation Function	Strategic Planning Group
1. Ensures that projects have the resources needed to be successful	8	3 / 24	5 / 40	3 / 24	1 / 8
2. Creates alignment with leaders from across the organization about the projects selected	10	1 / 10	5 / 50	3 / 30	1 / 10
3. Will take more project risks than are currently being taken	7	3 / 21	3 / 21	5 / 35	3 / 21
4. Builds capacity for the future	5	3 / 15	5 / 25	3 / 15	3 / 15
5. Does not significantly increase number of people needed to run the system	8	3 / 24	5 / 40	1 / 8	3 / 24
6. Costs less than $100K to implement (not including head counts)	6	5 / 30	3 / 18	5 / 30	3 / 18
Totals		124	194	142	96

17

SOLUTION DEFINITION

Create a contract for developing the solution

The *Solution Definition* tool produces a Solution Definition Document (SDD), which is simply a compilation of all the work that the team completed during the Gap Analysis and Solution Definition Stages. The SDD lays out the analyses and syntheses that led the team to the solution they believe will most effectively and efficiently address the need originally defined by the customer at the beginning of the Gap Analysis Stage.

Why do it?

- To communicate how the team arrived at its recommendation for a solution.

- To create a contract between the innovation team, the customer, the stakeholders, the sponsor, and the resource managers for what will be developed during the Development Stage.

What does it do?

- Captures the gap analysis, solution definition, and resource data that have been generated relative to the selected solution. Defines the scope and boundaries of the solution to be developed.

The Output of the Solution Definition Tool

What is the gap between what was and what could be?

Attach Needs Assessment, Cause Analysis, and Paradigm Deconstruction documentation

Solution Definition Document

Gap Defined

1. What are the problems with the current system, from the customer's point of view? What did the customer indicate they would like to see in a future solution?

2. What impact do the problems have on the business now? What would the impact be if the problems were not resolved? What impact would a new solution

3. What Type of Innovation is it and w

4. If it's an improvement project (type causes of the problem?

5. If it's a Type 3/4 project, what are rules and assumptions associated w

Attach documentation such as:
- *Solution Synthesis*
- *Paradigm Construction*
- *Solution Filter*
- *Technical Difficulty, Solution Impact Risk, and Adoption Assessment*
- *Vision Decomposition*
- *Solution Criteria & DC Prioritization and Solution Selection*
- *Project Plan*

Solution Selected

1. What solution options were consi

2. If the innovation is a reinvention o new paradigm what will be used t

3. What criteria were used to filter t ones were chosen for the study?

4. What assessment and other data filtered solutions?

5. What solution was selected and

6. If a Type 2, 3, or 4 innovation, wha solution and what are the staged

7. What actual characteristics will b staged solution? What were the customer's prioritized desired characteristics? Explain any differences.

Resources Required

Timeline information   Effort information
Cost information   Other resource information

Signatures Required

Sponsor   Innovation team members
Innovation leader   Customer or customer representatives
Key stakeholders   Resource managers

What is the best possible solution for solving the problem or capturing the opportunity?

What resources will be needed to develop and implement the solution?

Who needs to commit to the project moving into the development stage?

How do I do it?

✍ **1. Describe the gap between what is and what could be, which the identified solution was intended to close.**

😊 Answer the following questions and attach the applicable documents:

- What are the problems with the current system from the customer's point of view? (*Needs Assessment* tool).

- What impact do the problems have on the customer's business now? What would the impact be if the problem was not resolved or the opportunity not captured? (*Needs Assessment* tool).

- What was the customer's wish list for a solution? (*Needs Assessment* tool).

- What Type of Innovation is it and why? (Type 1, 2, 3, or 4?).

- If it's an improvement effort, what is causing the problem? (*Cause Analysis* tool).

- If it's a reinvention or invention effort, what is the paradigm of the current system? (*Paradigm Deconstruction* tool).

✍ **2. Describe the best possible solution to the problem and document why it was selected.**

😊 Answer the following questions and attach the applicable documents:

- What solution options were considered? (*Solution Construction* tool).

- If the innovation is a reinvention or invention, what is the new paradigm that will be the basis of the new solution? (*Paradigm Construction* tool).

- What Go/No Go criteria were used to filter the solutions, and which solutions were chosen for further study? (*Solution Filter* tool).

- What assessment and other data were collected about the filtered solutions?

  - What technical hurdles will have to be overcome and how will the team deal with those? Attach the Technical Difficulty Assessment Table. (*Technical Difficulty Assessment* tool).

  - What negative impacts could the solution have on its environment after it's launched? What plan does the team have to reduce the risk associated with those impacts? Attach the Solution Impact Risk Assessment table and the grid diagram. (*Solution Impact Risk Assessment* tool).

  - What resistance factors might get in the way of adoption of the solution and what plan does the team have for removing them? Attach the Adoption Assessment Table and the grid diagram. (*Adoption Assessment* tool).

- Which solution was selected and why? What were the criteria used? Attach the *Solution Selection Matrix*. (*Solution Selection* tool).

- If the innovation is a Type 2, 3, or 4 project, what is the long-term vision of the solution and how will the innovation be staged? (*Vision Decomposition* tool).

- What actual characteristics will be included in the first staged solution? (*Solution Selection* tool).

- What were the customer's prioritized Desired Characteristics (DCs)? (*Solution Criteria & DC Prioritization* tool).
- Explain any differences between the actual characteristics to be included and those requested by the customer (DCs).

3. Define the resources required to develop and implement the solution.

- Using a project management methodology, create a resource plan for the project. How much time will it take to complete the first staged project? How much effort? Money?
  - Make sure the team includes time to implement the countermeasures calculated in the *Technical Difficulty Assessment*, *Solution Impact Risk Assessment*, and *Adoption Assessment* tools.
  - Make sure the team includes contingency time, effort, and money in the plan to address any unexpected problems that undoubtedly will occur.

4. Acquire signatures of agreement for moving the solution forward into development as specified in the *Solution Definition Document*.

- The *Solution Definition Document* represents an agreement for moving forward into the Development Stage. It addresses both scope (what will be produced) as well as resources required.

- Get signatures of agreement from all the parties who will be involved in the development project. The signed Solution Definition Document then becomes the binding document for moving forward.

TIP

Make sure there is a change management procedure in place so that as things change during the development stage, which they inevitably will, the team is able to amend the Solution Definition Document.

18
COMMUNICATION PLAN

Who needs to know what, when, and how?

Communicating appropriately is key to moving the adoption process forward. With the *Communication Plan* tool, the team creates a plan for communicating with the customer, sponsor, and stakeholders that addresses the questions they have about the creation and adoption of the solution. In addition, the plan outlines how each message will be delivered, to whom, how often, etc.

Why do it?

To move the adoption process along by making sure the customer, sponsor, and stakeholders have the information they need about the solution being developed.

What does it do?

Identifies the key messages, the medium through which those messages will be delivered, the people who need to hear the message, how often, and who is accountable for each. Also identifies the features or characteristics of each medium of communication.

What medium will we use to communicate the message?

What do people want to know?

To whom do we need to communicate?

What do we need to tell them?

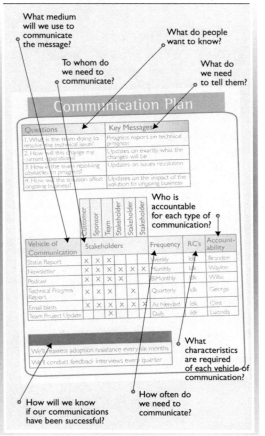

Communication Plan

Questions	Key Messages
1. What is the team doing to resolve the technical issue?	Progress report on technical progress
2. How will this change my current operations?	Updates on exactly what the changes will be
3. How is the team resolving obstacles to progress?	Updates on issues resolution
4. How will the solution affect ongoing business?	Updates on the impact of the solution to ongoing business

Who is accountable for each type of communication?

Vehicle of Communication	Stakeholders						Frequency	RC's	Account-ability
	Customer	Sponsor	Team	Stakeholder	Stakeholder	Stakeholder			
Status Report	X	X	X				Weekly	Idk	Brandon
Newsletter	X	X	X	X	X	X	Monthly	Idk	Waylon
Podcast	X	X	X	X			BiMonthly	Idk	Willie
Technical Progress Report	X	X	X		X		Quarterly	Idk	George
Email blasts	X	X	X	X	X	X	As Needed	Idk	Clint
Team Project Update			X				Daily	Idk	Lucinda

We'll reassess adoption resistance every six months

We'll conduct feedback interviews every quarter

What characteristics are required of each vehicle of communication?

How will we know if our communications have been successful?

How often do we need to communicate?

How do I do it?

✒ **1. What questions and concerns might the customer, sponsor, and stakeholders have about the progress of creating the solution during the Development and Implementation stages? Select the questions that need to be addressed with a communication plan.**

If the team did a Context Diagram, then the team has already identified the stakeholders. If the team did not create a Context Diagram, then do that first to identify the stakeholders for the final solution.

☺ Brainstorm all the questions and concerns the customer, stakeholders, and sponsor might have about the innovation effort.

- What questions might they have about the creation of the solution?

- What concerns would they have that could affect their adoption of the solution?

If the team did the Adoption Assessment, then the areas of concern about adoption have already been identified (resistance factors).

- Rewrite each concern as a question.

☺ Select the questions that need to be addressed in order to ensure the creation and adoption processes move along smoothly.

✐ **2. Determine the key messages—the "what" the team needs to say—to answer each question selected in Step 1.**

☺ Brainstorm how you could address each selected question. Remember your goal is to

- ☞ calm fear-based emotions.
- ☞ reduce their pain.
- ☞ reduce resistance.
- ☞ paint a positive vision of the future.
- ☞ demonstrate benefits of the solution.
- ☞ show how the invention will deal with unsolved problems.
- ☞ maintain support for the innovation project.

✐ **3. Determine the vehicles through which communications will be delivered.**

☺ How will the messages be delivered? This is the form the communication will be delivered in.

- ☞ Web site? Newsletter? Report?

✐ **4. For each vehicle (communication type), determine which stakeholder groups should receive the communication.**

✐ **5. Determine the frequency of communication.**

☺ How often will communications be delivered?

- ☞ Daily? Weekly? Monthly? Bimonthly? Quarterly?

6. Define any Required Characteristics (RCs) associated with each communication type.

☺ What requirements does the team have for each of the types of communications?

ↄ What features or functions need to be included?

7. Agree on accountability for each medium.

☺ Someone on the team will need to accept accountability for each of the communication mediums.

ↄ To be accountable is to ensure that the communication takes place effectively.

CASE STUDY

The innovation team at CLO Unlimited, a clinical laboratory company, came up with an online sales management system as a solution that will provide senior leaders with real-time access to the status of various aspects of the sales cycle, including status of new accounts, upcoming clinical trial RFPs, the company's bidding process, as well as status on contract preparation. The innovation team had already conducted an *Adoption Assessment* and brought up a number of concerns with the existing system.

---

8. Determine how the team will assess the success of the communications.

- How will the team know if the communication has been successful?

- What will the audience specifically start doing or stop doing?

- How will the team know if the communication plan is moving the adoption process forward?

CASE STUDY

The team spent some time considering how they would know whether their communication efforts were accomplishing what they wanted them to accomplish. Since the intent of the communication plan was to move the adoption process forward, they decided they would assess how that process was progressing in order to know if the communication plan was successful.

They decided to put a survey on the web site every month and ask all the stakeholders to complete it. As an incentive to fill out the survey, they would award a prize to one of the people who completed the survey. In addition, they would track who completed the surveys (not the results) and feed that information back to the managers. The survey would indicate how people were thinking and feeling about the new online system. If the trend was from negative to positive, then they would consider the communications plan a success.

19

CREATIVE PROBLEM SOLVING

Solve any problem

As the innovation team moves through the Development, Implementation, and Launch Stages, they will encounter problems—things that don't turn out as the team had planned or expected they would. In order to get back on track, these problems need to be solved. That is what the *Creative Problem Solving* tool is intended to do.

The steps in the creative problem-solving process are shown on page 218. They might look vaguely familiar, and that is because they are very similar to the basic steps of the innovation process. Problem solving begins with defining the criteria for a solution to the problem, then ideas are generated for a solution, those ideas are analyzed, and then the best idea is selected for implementation.

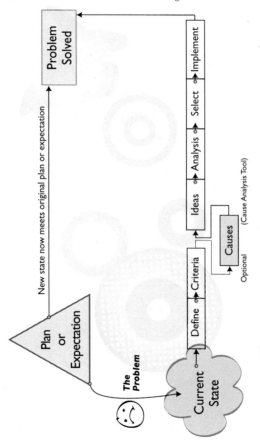

The differences between problem solving and innovation are:

Problem-Solving Process

- The GOAL is to return to the planned/expected state
- Can be a relatively quick response
- Has relatively few steps

Innovation Process

- The GOAL is to reach an entirely new state
- Usually takes time to come up with the innovative solution and then to develop and implement it
- Has more steps than problem solving and the more complex the innovation, the more steps there are

Why do it?

- Using a structured process helps to ensure that steps aren't skipped.

- It makes the problem-solving process visible to the team and stakeholders.

- It allows the team to participate in solving the problem and to arrive at consensus around which solution is best.

What does it do?

Defines the problem, generates ideas for solutions, analyzes those ideas, and then selects the best solution for implementation.

How do I do it?

 1. Define the urgency and scope of the problem to be solved. Who are the stakeholders and what is the impact of the problem on them? Define the state that should exist after the problem is solved.

A problem is a negative deviation from what was expected. (When things go better than expected, we don't call it a problem, we call it good luck!) When problems arise, we don't have to BE negative about them, nor should problems be excuses to place blame. It's much more helpful to stay neutral or to consider them opportunities in disguise. Follow the steps for creatively solving the problem and see if there isn't some unexpected gold hidden in the problem.

TIP

 Define the urgency of the problem:

- **High**—Crisis. Consequences are immediate and significant.

    - Use crisis management steps. (See Sidebar: "In a Crisis" on page 224).

    - When the problem is no longer a crisis, return to the steps for problem solving.

- **Medium**—Consequences are not immediate, but the problem is growing.
  - Implement short-term measures, if needed, to stop its growth, and then walk through problem-solving steps.
- **Low**—Consequences are not immediate and not growing.
  - Walk through methodology before implementing a solution.

- Define the scope of the problem.
  - Define the current state. What was expected to happen? What is the problem?
    - If applicable:
      - How big is the problem?
      - What is the frequency of the problem?
      - Is it recurring? A one-time incident?
      - What is not part of the problem?
      - What conditions need to exist for the problem to appear?

- Who is being affected by the problem? Who are the stakeholders?

- What is the impact of the problem on the stakeholders?

- Define the state that will be achieved when the problem is solved. This is the goal state, which is the state the team would like to have in place once the problem is solved.
  - Can the problem be reframed as an opportunity? When a problem arises it's a good time to step back and reassess whether the goal/plan you originally had is still the best future state to shoot for.

Is there a state that would be more desirable than the one originally planned or expected? If so, define the new goal state.

It's June 25th, and the innovation team at Longevity, a large hospital system, is in the development stage of creating an Innovation Project Management System (IPMS) for the organization. One of the elements in their development plan is to provide awareness training to the entire leadership team on what an IPMS entails and what changes will be required at Longevity in order to implement one.

The team contracted with an outside training company that specializes in innovation training to provide the leadership awareness training on two dates: July 14th and 28th. There is a 50 percent penalty clause in the contract if the workshops are cancelled within 30 days of delivery and so the team is already committed to the July 14th date unless they want to forfeit half of their workshop fee. The leaders were given the option of attending either one of the sessions and, so far, only 30 percent of the leaders have signed up for either of the two sessions. The team has defined the problem as follows:

continued...

❑ Urgency—Medium: In 3 days the team will be committed to paying a penalty if they have to cancel the July 28th date.

> Scope:
>
> > ❑ Current state: Only 30 percent of the leaders have signed up for one of the two workshops already scheduled for July 14th and 28th.
> >
> > ❑ Original Goal State: 100 percent attendance by leaders.
> >
> > ❑ Who affected (stakeholders): innovation project team, training company, leaders.
> >
> > ❑ Impact: There is a financial impact to the project, and there is an impact to the leaders if they don't get the training and, therefore, don't have the knowledge they need to implement the system being designed.

❑ Problem reframing: The team decided to view the problem as an opportunity. They decided that focusing on getting the leaders to training could provide an opportunity to educate them about why the training is important, which could enhance the adoption process.

❑ New Goal: 90 percent participation in training. The team felt that 90 percent participation was a more realistic goal in light of the fact that the workshop sessions were being held during the high season.

In a Crisis:

Stay calm, don't panic

Implement your contingency plan, if you have one.

❑ If there is no plan, take as much time as you can to plan how to respond.

Define the problem, and the impact of the problem.

❑ The problem is _____.

❑ If we don't fix this problem by _____, _____ will occur.

Address highest impact effects first.

Once the situation is stabilized:

❑ Plan next steps to stabilize further.

❑ Begin working through problem-solving steps.

✐ 2. Define the criteria for selecting a solution to the problem.

☺ Create a short list of criteria for picking a solution to the problem.

  ◉ Three to five criteria will be sufficient for most short-term problems.

  ◉ If the team is working on solving a longer-term problem or is seeking to find a permanent solution to a chronic problem, then five to ten criteria are recommended.

☺ Select criteria that are consistent with the goal state that the team is trying to achieve.

For problems that will generate a significant implementation effort to resolve, use the Solution Criteria and Desired Characteristics Prioritization tool to generate criteria for selection.

CASE STUDY

The team brainstormed criteria and narrowed them down to three:

A. The solution to the problem would prepare the leadership team for implementation of the IPMS.

B. The solution would not cost any more than was originally budgeted for the training.

C. The solution would be completed by August 15th, the date slated for the pilot of the design.

✐ 3. Optional: If the problem is recurring and the team is seeking a long-term solution, then identify the causes of the problem.

Use the Cause Analysis tool to analyze causes.

4. Generate ideas for a solution.

Brainstorm ideas for solving the problem.

- If the team did a cause analysis in Step 3, then brainstorm ideas for eliminating the causes.
- Use the rules of brainstorming from page 113.

See the Idea Generation tool for ways to generate ideas.

CASE STUDY

The team came up with a variety of ideas:

Have the training company provide the training as a series of webinars

Call each leader personally to explain the importance of the training and to schedule them for a session

Ask the CEO to send out a message that requires the leaders to go to training

Provide an incentive for leaders to sign up for training

Hold the training session and videotape it to show to leaders when they are available (with permission from the training company)

Do a communication blast to share the importance of the training

---

✐ 5. Analyze the ideas.

(☺) Sort the ideas into two categories:

- ☞ Category 1—ideas that the team assesses would allow them to reach the new goal state, and

- ☞ Category 2—ideas that will not allow the team to reach the new goal state.

(☺) Filter the ideas in Category 1 through the criteria selected in Step 2.

(☺) Identify the strengths and weaknesses of each idea that meet the criteria.

Alternatively, the team can use the S/W/C tool to analyze ideas as outlined in Step 4 of the Solution Filter tool.

CASE STUDY

The team analyzed the ideas and found that four of them ended up in Category 1. They then filtered them through the criteria and evaluated the strengths and weaknesses of the three that met the criteria. The criteria were:

A. The solution to the problem would prepare the leadership team for implementation of the IPMS.

B. The solution would not cost any more than was originally budgeted for the training.

C. The solution would be completed by August 15th, the date slated for the pilot of the design.

continued...

Category I - Will help reach the goal	Criteria A = Prep Leaders	Criteria B = Same Cost	Criteria C = August 15th	Strengths	Weaknesses
		Criteria		Strengths	Weaknesses
1. Have the training company provide the training as a series of webinars	✓			Solution not chosen— did not meet criteria	
2. Call each leader personally to explain the importance of the training and to schedule them for a session	✓	✓	✓	The phone call would be an opportunity to "sell" them the solution	None
3. Hold the training session and videotape it to show to leaders at a variety of dates after 7/14 (with permission from the training company)	✓	✓	✓	A variety of dates could be offered for the training by video or the leaders could watch it on their own	Less interest from those who would want to watch just a video; the workshop is experiential and watching it will not be the same as experiencing it
4. Do a communication blast to share the importance of the training	✓	✓	✓	Provides another opportunity to "sell" the solution	None

6. Select the solution to the problem.

Choose the solution that best matches the criteria and whose strengths outweigh the weaknesses.

If the team is solving a major problem and there is no clear solution, then consider using the Solution Selection tool to select the best possible solution to the problem.

CASE STUDY

The team decided they would combine ideas #2 and #4: Do a communication blast about the importance of the training and then personally call each leader to further sell them on the importance of the training and to book them for one of the two training sessions.

---

7. Plan and implement the solution.

Create an implementation plan:

- How will the solution be implemented? Who will be accountable to make sure it's implemented?

- What tasks must be accomplished to implement the solution? How long will each task take? What is the deadline for implementation? Are there resources available for help with implementation?

Execute the implementation plan.

The team discussed who would be accountable for creating the communications. They then divided up the names of the leaders who had not signed up for training between the six members of the team, so each member only had to call ten leaders. There was no guarantee that leaders who had already signed up would automatically attend, so the team decided to call those leaders and reinforce how important it was for them to attend the training.

20
MODELING THE SOLUTION

Get feedback on the solution as it's being built

To model an improvement or invention is to provide the customer with approximations of how the final solution will look and how it will function throughout the development process. Architects, for example, create blueprints, and/or computer simulations, and/or scale models so the customer can better visualize the project. This is called progressive modeling.

Progressive modeling offers these benefits:

The description of the solution that the team put together in the Solution Description Document is a written description; therefore it's abstract. Most people are concrete thinkers; therefore they can't truly conceptualize what it is they will be receiving simply by reading a list of the features and functions. Progressive modeling provides them with something more concrete to react to.

It allows for early feedback on whether or not the solution will meet the customer's needs and expectations. The earlier you start modeling, the better.

It allows the customer to begin the process of attaching to the new solution and letting go of the method. The more interactions the customer has with the new solution, the easier it is for her to see herself using it.

It helps the team "sell" the solution to stakeholders resistant to change.

Principles for Modeling

1. The more complex the solution, the more important it is for the team to model it.

Complex solutions are harder for the customer to visualize. Whenever possible, provide the customer with a model of the final solution.

2. The more complex the solution, the more iterations of the solution the team should be modeling for the customer.

The more complex the solution that is to be developed, the more difficult it is to specify, at the end of the *Solution Definition Stage*, all the features and functions that the final solution should include. Instead, model iterations of the final solution and get feedback from the customer so the next stage of development can be targeted to what the customer needs and wants.

3. The greater the paradigm shift represented by the solution, the more important it is to model.

- When the team is working on a Type One (minor improvement) innovation, there is little need to model it because the difference between the solution being developed and the current system is not a major shift.

(☺) Major improvements, reinventions, and inventions (Types 2, 3, and 4) call for modeling because the shift from the current system to the future solution is significant.

✍️ 4. Use a model that is as close to the solution as possible.

For example, a scale model is closer to a real building than is a drawing. Try to make the model as tangible as possible (again this helps with concrete thinking).

✍️ 5. When possible, create ways for the customer to experience the solution, to interact with it.

This not only improves the quality of the feedback that the customer can provide, but it also helps the customer to move toward adopting the solution because he has had the chance to "use" it.

Ways in which to Model.

(☺) If the team is working on a solution that is a product:

- (◉) Is there a way to create a computer 3-D model of the final product?

- (◉) Can the team create a scale model? A prototype?

- (◉) Can the team modify an existing product so it can simulate the features of the new one being developed?

(☺) If the team is working on a solution that is a service (the act of one person doing for another—a human interaction):

- Model the existing service scenarios using role plays. Then model the new service scenarios with role plays. This will allow the customer to experience the difference between the old service and the new one.

- If the team is working on a solution that is a process:

  - Think about how the team can get the customer to experience the problems of the old process and then experience what it will be like operating the new process. One way to do this is to create a simulation of the process using a board game. The essential elements of the old process are captured in a game and then the game is changed to simulate the new process. The game process allows leaders and workers to experience the shift that will need to be made to move from the old process to the new one.

  - Animated computer simulation software can illustrate how the process is working using bar or pie charts that vary with changes over time, or as input values are readjusted.

- If the team is working on a solution that's a system:

  - Systems are more complex than products, services, or processes, and so are more difficult to model. In software development, progressive modeling is called agile development. Progressive iterations of the final system are developed and shared with the customer. The customer provides feedback on how the system is progressing, which drives the next iteration of development. This allows the parts of the system to be completed (and potentially implemented) while other parts are still in development and allows for an iterative design and continual feedback on how the design is progressing.

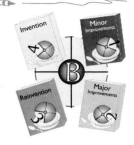

21

TESTING
THE SOLUTION

Check technical and adoption progress

Testing is a way to make sure that when the team reaches the end of the innovation process, the solution they produce delivers on what was promised in the Solution Definition Document. It can also be a way of collecting data about how the development of the solution is progressing, which can then be used to communicate progress to the customer, sponsor, and stakeholders.

There are three types of testing:

1. Testing the interim deliverables (ID) as they are produced during the Technical Development Process.

2. Testing partial solutions.

3. Testing the whole solution in a pilot.

The Types of Testing

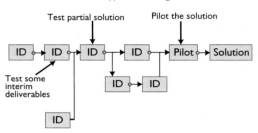

1. Test interim deliverables

Interim deliverables are the building blocks of the final solution. When building a house, the framed house is an interim deliverable (ID). IDs are handed off from one internal customer to the next. In the figure below, an ID is produced by Group A (ID1) and then handed off to Group B, who uses ID1 as an input to produce ID2. Group B must decide, before they accept ID1, if ID1 is acceptable to them, if it meets their criteria for acceptance.

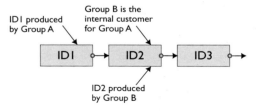

The Hand-Offs of Interim Deliverables (ID)

To ensure that each interim deliverable is accepted by the next customer in the chain, try the following tips:

✒ Collect acceptance criteria from the next customer in the chain.

- Make sure you know exactly what the customer of the interim deliverable needs and wants from the deliverable you're producing. (This is called acceptance criteria.)

- If it's the first time you've produced this type of interim deliverable, or if there have been problems in the past, negotiate the characteristics of the interim deliverable with the next customer to make sure you'll be delivering what they need.

- Make sure the next customer's acceptance criteria are aligned with what the ultimate customer wants from the final solution.

✒ Design tests to make sure the interim deliverables works properly before it is handed off to the next customer in the chain.

- How can you test the interim deliverable to make sure it performs as required?

✒ Conduct reviews of the interim deliverable before handing it off to the next customer.

- A review is the perusal of the interim deliverable by another party. Ask technical experts to review the interim deliverable to make sure it matches the criteria for acceptance before handing it off to the next customer in the process.

2. Test partial solutions

When we test interim deliverables, we are testing them against the acceptance criteria of the next customer in the chain. When we test partial solutions, we are testing them against the criteria (characteristics) established in the Solution Definition Document. The types of solutions that lend themselves to testing partial solutions are ones that can be created using a modular design. For example, if you were creating a training solution, you could create the workshop in modules, and then test the success of each module with the customer, rather than waiting until the whole training program was developed before testing it.

✍ As the team completes a portion of the solution, have it tested by the final customer.

- Testing the module or partial solution provides feedback on whether you're heading in the right direction and allows you to make modifications and change directions if needed, before the whole solution is built. In addition, it gives the customer a chance to get used to the solution as it's being built. This moves the adoption process forward.

✍ Publicize successes.

- Success stories support the adoption process. Communicate positive results from the tests via the Communication Plan in order to spread the good news.

- Also explain what didn't work and what the team is doing to fix the problem.

A test of the full solution is called a pilot. The pilot can be either a sample of the final solution (such as a pilot batch from smaller-scale manufacturing equipment that tests the manufacturing process and the product produced), or testing the entire solution with a subset of the customer base.

☞ Pilot the process on a smaller scale than the final process.

ⓣ Run the process on smaller-scaled equipment to test how well the process works and the quality of the product.

   ◦ Test the product to determine if it meets specifications.

   ◦ Test the product in actual use by the customer, if possible, to see if it meets their needs.

   ◦ Evaluate the amount of variation to expect when the pilot is taken to full scale.

☞ Pilot the final solution with a small subset of the customer base.

ⓣ Do a preliminary launch with a small group of customers, to test:

   ◦ How the solution works.

   ◦ How easily the solution is adopted.

   ◦ Whether your implementation/launch plan works.

ⓣ Consider the pilot group carefully.

   ◦ You're looking to test if the solution works, so you want a sample population that will provide feedback similar to that which you would expect from any customer group. That being said, it's also good to pilot with a supportive group that will be excited about the change and that will act as change agents as the solution is rolled out during the Implementation Stage.

- Determine what feedback the team will need as a result of the test.

  - What data do you need to collect? What will you use as a baseline for comparison?

  - How will you know what needs to be revised when the test is over?

  - Make sure to include adoption feedback and not just technical feedback.

Publicize what worked during the pilot and how the team is addressing any problems that were encountered.

22

LAUNCHING THE SOLUTION

Implementing the solution

By the time the team makes it to the Implementation Stage, the creation process should be about 98 percent complete. If the team has done a good job of testing the deliverables and piloting the solution, the characteristics and performance measures of the solution should match what was stipulated in the Solution Definition Document, and, therefore, should meet the needs of the customer and key stakeholders. The only thing left in the creation process is attending to any unforeseen "bugs" that might come up as the solution gets wider use during the Implementation Stage. (However, in some industries, like pharmaceuticals, the solution must be at the 100 percent level before implementation; certainly in any industry, 100 percent should be the goal.)

Because Creation is essentially complete, the Implementation Stage is all about adoption. And, as we discussed way back in Chapter 1, gathering momentum for adoption starts on Day 1 with the *Needs Assessment* tool so that by the time the team gets to launch, the foundations for adoption should be firmly in place and the customer should be eagerly awaiting the solution!

✐ **Pull the launch team together.**

🕲 The launch team should include team members who were also part of the development effort. This provides continuity between stages.

✐ **Create a launch plan.**

🕲 Don't wait until development is over to begin planning for launch. The size of the launch and the level of difficulty of the adoption will determine how early you need to start the planning process.

🕲 The Launch Plan should include:

- **A rollout plan**—How the solution will be rolled out, especially if there is more than one customer group.

  - Consider phasing in the solution in small, fast doses versus one large rollout. This makes for a more manageable rollout and gives you time to learn and adjust before the rollout to the next customer group.

- **A communication plan**—The team will need a new communication plan for launch. For external launches, this will include the marketing plan. For internal launches, the communication plan is the internal marketing plan.

- **A resource plan**—How much time, effort, and money will be required to complete the launch? Use your project management toolbox to create a resource plan.

- **Risk assessment**—What risks might be encountered during launch and how can the team prevent or mitigate those risks?

- **Support services plan**—Plan for support services during the launch. Even if the quality of the product is at 100 percent, there are bound to be questions and concerns about this new solution. Brainstorm in advance the questions that you might receive from customers and be prepared with the answers.

- **Measurement plan**—What kind of feedback should the team collect as it rolls out the solution to the first customer group? What will be measured? How will that information be used? What is the plan to factor that feedback information into the next rollout?

During Launch

✐ **Collect feedback data.**

The team should be collecting feedback data from the rollout to the first customer group so it can improve the way it rolls out the solution to the next group and then to the next.

Feedback will also be provided from the customer about the solution itself. If the feedback is that the solution DOES NOT meet the agreements in the *Solution Selection Document* (SSD), then the team has a Problem, and should use the *Creative Problem Solving* tool to work through what to do to solve the problem. (To avoid the problem in the future, make sure that the SSD is agreed to and then see the *Modeling the Solution & Testing the Solution* tools.)

If the solution does meet the agreed-on performance levels or characteristics as agreed to in the SSD, then congratulations—you've done a great job!

References

Fritz, Robert. 1989. *The Path of Least Resistance: Learning to Become the Creative Force in Your Own Life.* New York, NY: Random House.

Index

The Innovation Tools Memory Jogger™ | ©2009 GOAL/QPC